Bridges of Bedford:

by

Angela Simco & Peter McKeague

Published jointly by

Bedfordshire County Council
Bedfordshire Archaeological Council
Royal Commission on the Historical Monuments of England

Bedfordshire Archaeology Occasional Monograph Series
No 2   1997

BEDFORDSHIRE ARCHAEOLOGY
OCCASIONAL MONOGRAPH SERIES
No 2, 1997

Edited by Evelyn Baker and Stephen Coleman

Contributions to the occasional monograph series and county journal *Bedfordshire Archaeology*
should be sent to the Assistant Editor at
19 Coronation Road, Cranfield, Bedfordshire, MK43 0JP (Tel. 01234 751453)

Intending contributors are asked to format articles as set out in the Contributors' Notes,
available from the Assistant Editor

Front cover: Turvey bridge from the south-west
Stone-for-stone drawing of Sutton bridge, south face

CONTENTS

FOREWORD

This second volume in the Bedfordshire Archaeology Monograph Series is a tribute to the co-operation at both local and national level which enabled the successful execution of the conservation and recording project whose results are presented here.

Historic bridges, as a class of monument, lie on the interface between the related disciplines of archaeology and historic buildings studies. They may be complex, multi-period structures, requiring detailed interpretation and chronological analysis; or they may be single-phase artefacts, representing a particular stage in the evolution of architectural and engineering skills. They are perhaps subject to more physical pressures than any other class of monument, as traffic volume and weight increases almost inexorably.

In 1982, the then County Surveyor embarked upon a comprehensive programme to bring the county's stock of historic bridges into a good state of repair. The recently passed Ancient Monuments and Archaeological Areas Act (1979) provided the legal framework for the repair schemes to be carried out in a way which respected the individual historic character of each bridge, and of which archaeological recording was an integral part. Recognising both the opportunity and the need for research and methodological development which a project of this scale presented, English Heritage funded the County Planning Department's Conservation Section for the first full two years of recording. The value of a complete historical record of each bridge was soon demonstrated, providing as it did a datum from which practical decisions could be taken to meet both engineering and conservation requirements. The resulting methodology and procedure stands as a model of best practice for any similar schemes or programmes.

The analysis of a group of related monuments within a geographical area also reflects the aims and objectives of the Royal Commission on the Historical Monuments of England. It is therefore fitting that this publication should be a joint venture between the Commission, the County Council and Bedfordshire Archaeological Council.

John Hawksby
Chairman
Bedfordshire County Council

Ron Fowler
Chairman
Bedfordshire Archaeological Council

Tom Hassall
Secretary & Chief Executive
Royal Commission on the Historical
Monuments of England

ACKNOWLEDGEMENTS

Many people have assisted with the preparation of this volume, to whom I offer my personal thanks:-

Peter McKeague, who undertook much of the research and fieldwork and must take most of the credit for the development of the recording methodology; and who produced most of the draft reports from which this final version has been edited.

David Baker, for his support and encouragement over the years, and for his persistence in seeing this publication through to its completion.

English Heritage, for funding the first two years of recording, and especially for the advice of Inspectors David Sherlock, Anthony Streeten and Deborah Priddy.

The County Engineer and his staff, for financial support and co-operation during repair contracts, especially Peter Tobutt, Rajni Vasani and John Slinn.

The Royal Commission on the Historical Monuments of England, for a generous grant towards publication, and to John Bold for his comments on a draft text.

The County Archivist and his staff.

John Johnson, Jim Godfrey and Conrad Shafie of the County Council's Graphics Team for producing finished copies of the drawings.

The County Photographer, Dave Stubbs.

Patricia Bell, Stephen Coleman, Martin Cook and Alan Cox for provision of additional information and much helpful advice.

Original drawings are by Peter McKeague and Angela Simco, unless otherwise acknowledged. Photographs, except where indicated, are from the historic bridge archives now held by the Heritage and Environment Advisory Team in the Department of Environment and Economic Development, Bedfordshire County Council.

The summary was translated into French by Jillian Greenwood and Maxine Copeland, and into German by Ruth Gibson.

Angela Simco
March 1997

INTRODUCTION

In 1982, Bedfordshire's County Surveyor embarked on a comprehensive programme of repairs to those of the county's historic bridges which lie on the public highway. At the time of writing, eleven of these are scheduled as ancient monuments of national importance, and six listed as buildings of special historic or architectural importance. This placed legal restraints upon the extent and character of repairs, and offered a technical challenge in reconciling the demands of modern traffic with the need to conserve these much-valued historic features in the Bedfordshire landscape. It also presented an unparalleled opportunity for the investigation and recording of the county's bridges as a group of related monuments.

In response, the Conservation Section of the County Planning Department established a programme of research and recording which ensured that the distinctive historic character of each bridge could be understood and respected in the design of repairs, and that any information revealed during the repair schemes would be fully recorded. This volume presents the results of this research and recording programme.

The archaeological recording methodology was developed with the help of a grant from English Heritage in 1986-88. Since then all recording has been financed by the County Surveyor as part of each repair scheme. The archaeological Project Manager for the Conservation Section was Angela Simco. Peter McKeague, Field Officer 1986-89, carried out the bulk of the documentary and field research, as well as providing on-site recording during the most active period of the repair programme. Further field recording was undertaken by Martin Cook, Field Officer 1989-92. Most of the draft text of this volume was prepared by Peter McKeague, and it has been edited for publication by Angela Simco, who takes responsibility for any errors or omissions.

Although research was targeted towards those of the county's bridges which were due for repair, it inevitably produced information on other bridges which have not survived, allowing broader themes to be drawn out and the surviving bridges to be better understood as a result. Less has been studied about private bridges away from the public highway (with the exception of Basin Bridge, Woburn Park, which was repaired by the Bedford Estate in 1992), mainly because fewer documents relating to their construction and maintenance are available. Most of the small rural bridges which were built in the second half of the 19th century have not been included here for reasons of space, though their value as familiar features of village and parish is not disputed; neither have railway bridges been covered. Information on many minor bridges can be found in the County Council's Historic Environment Record. St Neots and Hail bridges, though no longer situated within Bedfordshire, have been included as they lay within the county before modern boundary changes.

While there may have been some value in arranging the material chronologically, it has been presented topographically by river valley, in order to avoid the problem of multi-period bridges or bridge sites being split between different sections. Historical and technical themes are drawn out in the relevant summary chapters, and Appendix 1 provides a time chart of the major bridges for cross-reference.

RECORDING METHODOLOGY

The first stage of each repair scheme was the preparation of a stone-for-stone drawing of the bridge (produced either by photogrammetry or rectified photography). This provided a base plan both for more detailed historical analysis of the structure and for the preparation of engineering drawings for the repair contract. Historical information was gathered by close examination of the components of the visible structure, such as stone type and method of working, pointing techniques, special architectural features and evidence of alteration, extension or repair. Where a bridge had been altered over time, different phases could sometimes at this stage be correlated with work described in documentary records.

During the repair scheme, the removal of stonework, and any excavation of the foundations or the bridge deck, was monitored and recorded archaeologically. Further historic information was often revealed as older parts of the bridge were exposed to view.

After the completion of fieldwork, an archive for the bridge was compiled, comprising full documentary references, field records, photographs and analytical reports; each archive now forms the starting point for the management of future repairs. In view of the quantity of data involved, this present volume can only offer a summary of the results achieved.

THE HISTORY OF RESEARCH

The earliest interest shown in the history of bridges was for purely practical reasons: each County's Justices of the Peace, meeting in Quarter Sessions, needed to know who had built particular bridges (and therefore was legally responsible for their repair), so that they could ensure that they were properly maintained.

Some antiquaries took an interest in ancient bridges and described them in their travels round the country. For example, John Leland provides the earliest, albeit very brief, description of Barford bridge in the 16th century. The first detailed surveys of bridges also appear at this time, one for St Neots being particularly valuable. By the late 18th century bridges had become a popular feature in landscape drawings: in Bedfordshire, Thomas Fisher was a noted landscape artist of the early 19th century, who specialised in historic buildings and structures.

By the early 20th century wider studies developed. Inglis studied bridges in Scotland, attempting to characterise their features and trace their development. Jervoise and Henderson carried out valuable work on the ancient bridges of England and Wales. The Society for the Protection of Ancient Buildings funded Jervoise in the 1920s, partly in response to the increasing threat to bridges from road improvements; his book on *The Ancient Bridges of Mid and Eastern England* (1932) included the first general study of the bridges of Bedfordshire.

Photogrammetric records of Oxfordshire bridges were made in the late 1970s, but elsewhere the study of bridges as groups has been generally rare; Renn's treatment of Surrey's Wey valley bridges in 1974 is an exception. In France much more interest developed in medieval and later bridges, with notable studies by Boyer (1976), Mesqui (1986) and Prade (1986 and 1988).

The first comprehensive historical surveys of Bedfordshire bridges appeared in the *Lockgate* magazine between 1962 and 1969, written by Patricia Bell and Alan Cirket of the Bedfordshire Record Office. This present study is broader in scope, incorporating the results of recent archaeological research. It covers both the development of individual bridges and the overall evolution of bridge design across the county. It assesses the importance of local topography, maintenance liabilities, transport needs, the availability of raw materials, and the influence of wider architectural developments on local bridge construction.

HISTORICAL SUMMARY

THE EARLY HISTORY OF BRIDGES

In these days of convenient travel, it is easy to forget that rivers, and even minor streams, were often in the past a major obstacle to the movement of people and goods. The line of many ancient routeways was therefore strongly influenced by the position of suitable fording-places, and local communication was often dependent on small boats for access from one settlement to the next. From earliest times, available technology has been used where possible to provide more permanent crossings.

The earliest known structures took the form of causeways across marshy ground. The neolithic Sweet Track in the Somerset Levels has been dated by dendrochronology (tree-ring dating) to 3807/3806 BC.[1] From the Bronze Age, vertical timbers have been found in the edge of a silted river channel at Boveney in Buckinghamshire. These may have formed part of a bridge across an old course of the River Thames and date from about 1400/1300 BC. Nearby, two parallel lines of timbers going right across the channel were almost certainly from a later Iron Age bridge.[2]

The remains of several Roman bridges have been found in Britain. Most of them, for example Aldwincle, Northamptonshire,[3] and Ivy Farm, Fencott with Murcott, to the north of Otmoor in Oxfordshire,[4] were of wooden construction. In the north of England, bridges on the line of Hadrian's Wall at Willowford and Chesters were probably built entirely of stone; some bridges, such as at Piercebridge, Co Durham, had stone piers and abutments, but may have been spanned with timber.[5]

By the 8th century the repair of bridges was considered an obligation, along with military service and maintaining fortresses, from which no free man might be excused.[6] Their strategic importance is marked by the number of *burhs* (defended towns) which were established at crossings points during the Saxon period. The first bridge at Bedford may have been built to link the two halves of the town when Edward the Elder laid out the southern burh in 915 on the south side of the River Ouse.[7]

While Saxon bridges were probably mostly of timber (as indeed were many medieval ones), evidence for masonry construction emerges after the Norman Conquest, notably at Oxford, where the substantial remains of an early stone bridge can be seen buried in later widenings of the southern approaches to Folly bridge. This may be the *Grand Pont* built by Robert D'Oilly, Sheriff of Oxford in the late 11th century.[8]

THE NATURE OF THE EVIDENCE

In order to reconstruct the history of an individual bridge, it is necessary to draw on both archaeological evidence (the physical remains) and historic documents. Both of these sources of information have their limitations. Physical evidence disappears when bridges are altered or demolished, or river channels scoured; or it may not be easily accessible, buried below the river bed or locked within a later structure. The documentary record is incomplete, either because events were never written down or because only some of the relevant documents have survived. However, written sources are still a valuable tool. If treated carefully, much information about who built and maintained bridges, and about how attitudes to bridge maintenance changed over time, can be extracted. These are important factors in understanding the historic development and present appearance of many of the county's earlier bridges.

THE MEDIEVAL BRIDGE BUILDERS

In 1215, *Magna Carta* accepted that it was the responsibility of all free men (that is, of individuals rather than the state) to build and maintain bridges, but also declared that 'no manor or man shall be compelled to make bridges over the rivers except those which ought to do it of old were and rightfully'.[9] There was no further legislation during the medieval period specifically governing bridges, although the Statute of Winchester, 1285, affirmed that each lord of the manor was responsible for the upkeep of the King's Highway;[10] by implication this must have included any bridges on it. As a result, bridges rarely occur in state records; they were generally not the concern of the Crown except when neglected or in dispute.

It is not known who was responsible for the initial construction of Bedfordshire's earliest medieval bridges. The first occurrence in documents is often an incidental reference to a bridge as a land-mark (such as Turvey bridge in 1136/38). However, as the builder of a bridge was held responsible for subsequent repairs, the maintenance liabilities of later centuries can shed some light on who that may have been.

In rural areas, bridges were often the sole responsibility of the local **lord of the manor.** For example, Kempston Hardwick bridge was repaired by one of the three manors in Kempston in 1430. In some cases there was a complex arrangement of shared liability. The four main river arches of Harrold bridge were repaired by the lords of the manors of Harrold, Odell, Carlton and Chellington; as these four historic parishes met near the river crossing, it seems likely that the first bridge was a joint enterprise between all four manors.

In some cases, bridges were maintained by the **parish** as a whole, rather than by the lord of the manor as an individual. For example, the 'townships' (ie parishes) of Biddenham, Stagsden, Stevington and Turvey were charged with failing to repair Bromham bridge in 1383. However, written evidence of parish involvement in this early period is rare.

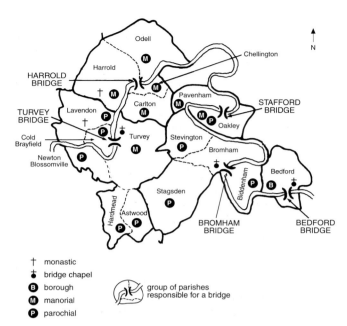

† monastic
‡ bridge chapel
🅑 borough
🅜 manorial
🅟 parochial

group of parishes
responsible for a bridge

Fig 1 Responsibilities for bridge maintenance in the upper Ouse valley

Monastic houses were frequently involved in bridge building and repair, both as an expression of piety, and because good communications helped the efficient administration of large monastic estates. At St Neots the townspeople took action against the Prior in 1349 for failing to repair the long causeway across the river meadows. Where medieval documents are absent, monastic involvement can still be deduced from later maintenance arrangements. After the Dissolution of the Monasteries in the 16th century, their repair liabilities were not transferred to the new landowners and subsequently fell to the Justices of the Peace for the County; bridges (or parts of bridges) for which the County was liable after the 16th century may therefore have been monastic in origin. This is probably the case at Harrold, where most of the long foot causeway, and the part of the river bridge which was not the responsibility of the local manors, may have been built by Harrold Priory.

The construction and upkeep of town bridges was usually more of a collective than an individual responsibility. Maintenance of Bedford bridge was the responsibility of the **Borough** as a whole; and when St Neots Priory failed in its duties, the bailiff and men of the town arranged for repairs to St Neots bridge.

Figure 1 shows the complex and varied liabilities for major bridges in the upper Ouse valley in the medieval period. While the responsibility for Bedford bridge lay only with the Borough, that for the great bridges of Bromham, Stafford, Harrold and Turvey was shared between several nearby parishes.

FINANCES

Apart from the personal or corporate finances of manorial

lords, monasteries and towns, additional revenue for bridge maintenance was raised from a number of sources.

Tolls were frequently collected on urban bridges, but because they affected the free movement of traffic on the king's highway they required the royal grant of **'pontage'**. This was particularly common in the 14th century, with the bridges at Bedford, Biggleswade and St Neots each receiving grants. Properties in Bedford were also dedicated by the Borough for bridge maintenance, with the **rents** being used for repairs.

On some bridges, **chapels** were founded, with a bridge priest or chaplain who would say masses for the dead in return for alms donated by passing travellers; the income would be used to maintain the bridge. The chapel associated with Bromham bridge received substantial gifts of houses and lands, providing additional revenue.

Biggleswade and St Neots bridges benefited from the sale of **indulgences,** whereby remission of sins was granted by the Church in return for pious donations.

Bridges were occasionally mentioned in **wills.** Usually a sum of money, or other goods, was bequeathed for repair work, though a more substantial bequest by Sir Gerard Braybroke in 1427/29 allowed for the construction of a new bridge at Great Barford. Over fifty bequests can be found amongst the wills of the Archdeaconry of Bedford, 1498-1526, and the Prerogative Court of Canterbury, 1383-1547, and in other catalogued references in the Bedfordshire Record Office.[11] Most examples date from the late 15th/early 16th century. There is a marked bias towards Ouse bridges, which perhaps reflects different survival rates for the source material but may also be an indication of the importance which was placed on those bridges.

Some benefactors left legacies only to small bridges in their own parish, like those in Pertenhall which benefited from the will of William Slade: in 1508 he left 'to Filbrigge 2s; to the bridge of the vill 2s; to the bridge called Walcard 2s'.[12] Other bridges received bequests from nearby parishes. Parishioners of Stevington, for example, left money to bridges which had enabled them to travel to Bedford (via Stafford or Bromham bridge), to Olney (Turvey bridge), or to Wellingborough and Northampton (Harrold bridge). Bequests from London merchants to Bedford and Bromham bridges highlight their significance as crossing points on major through routes. In some cases, **charities** were set up to maintain bridges. The earliest example is at Shefford in 1560, where a town charity to look after the bridges was created in a bequest. Sutton bridge benefited from charitable funds provided by John and Constance Burgoyne; this bequest rationalised previous manorial duties into a trust.

THE GROWING ROLE OF THE COUNTY

Henry VIII's reign saw significant legislation which affected the traditional mechanisms for maintaining bridges. Firstly, in 1530/31, 'an Act concerning the amendment [repair] of bridges in the Highways' was passed.[13]

This not only reaffirmed existing customs, but also for the first time required Justices of the Peace to raise a county rate for the repair of those bridges outside towns where no authority or individual could be proven responsible.

Secondly, the Acts of Dissolution of 1536 and 1539[14] broke up the monastic estates, many of which had built and maintained bridges, and transferred them to private owners. The new owners of monastic land did not inherit ancient obligations along with the rest of the property, and events at St Neots are a valuable illustration of this. Inquiries into the bridge by Commissioners for Queen Elizabeth in 1588 found that anciently the Priory had been largely responsible for the bridge, but since the Suppression (of the Priory) the inhabitants of the parish and various well-disposed people in the neighbouring counties had maintained the bridge.

In a similar move the property of chantry chapels, including those on bridges, was granted by Parliament to the King in 1545.[15] This was put into effect in Edward VI's reign and the chantries suppressed;[16] this completed the removal of ecclesiastical liability for bridges.

As a consequence of the 1530/31 Act, the County began to take responsibility for the repair of specific bridges (or parts of them). Work was administered by the Justices of the Peace, meeting in Quarter Sessions, and funded through local taxes. It appears that Bedfordshire was already raising a county rate for bridge repair in the 16th century: the 1588 Commission of Inquiry into St Neots bridge recognised that '... the inhabitants of Bedd'shire be grevously burdened taxed and charged with money and carriage for repaire of divers great bridges'.[17] In spite of this, the County was still instructed to carry out repairs at St Neots. Some of the 'divers great bridges' are identified in a survey of c1630 of bridges in Willey Hundred (which covered the upper Ouse valley), recording those parts of Bromham, Harrold and Stafford bridges which were repairable by the County.[18]

Few Quarter Sessions records survive before 1711, apart from one volume of the Minutes between 1650 and 1660; this includes instructions to repair Barford, Bromham and Harrold bridges in 1651.[19] Occasionally legal judgments were also given at the King's Summer or Winter Assizes: in 1671, for example, the County was found liable for the repair of Barford bridge.

In some counties during the late 17th and early 18th centuries, the bridge rate was used to build new bridges for public use. There is no evidence for such 'gratuity bridges' in Bedfordshire, but the practice was eventually restricted by a clause in the 1739 County Rate Act prohibiting any money being spent on bridge repairs 'until Presentment had been made by the Grand Jury, at the Assizes or Sessions, of their insufficiency, inconveniency, or want of reparation'.[20]

Until the end of the 18th century, the County bore responsibility (in whole or part) only for the great bridges of St Neots, Barford, Bromham, Stafford and Harrold. By this time more and more bridges were being built through private funds, by turnpike trusts, parishes or individuals.

Their builders frequently failed to maintain them, and the County was found responsible for ever-increasing numbers of bridges: by 1815, Beadlow, Shefford North and South, Radwell, Clay (in Clifton), Arlesey, Harrowden, Tempsford, Cranfield (in Westoning) and Hollington had been added to the list.

This problem was addressed to some extent in 1803, when an Act of Parliament, promoted by Lord Ellenborough, required that new, privately built, bridges should be constructed in a manner of which the Justices would approve, before the County could take over responsibility for repair.[21] For example, in 1821 John Morris, the Salford parish surveyor, requested an inspection of the new bridge at Low Bush, so that the bridge might thereafter be repaired by the County.[22] Not all newly built structures met the requirements: both Oakley bridge (built 1815) and Felmersham bridge (1818) were privately maintained long after construction.

Throughout the 18th century individual Justices supervised repairs, often carried out by locally appointed caretakers.

By 1816 the need for a full-time post was recognised; John Millington was appointed Surveyor of Bridges, and a separate committee was established to administer the surveyor's work.

THE TRANSPORT REVOLUTION

The development of the Turnpike road system from the late 17th century saw the improvement or construction of many bridges. For example, the Great North road was turnpiked in 1725 (from Biggleswade to Alconbury Hill) and 1730 (from Stevenage to Biggleswade).[23] The Turnpike Trust concerned itself not only with improvements to the road, but was responsible for the erection of Girtford bridge and a timber bridge at Tempsford, and co-operated with the County and the Ivel Navigation Commissioners to rebuild Biggleswade bridge. The Bedford to Olney Turnpike Trust undertook major work at Turvey bridge in the late 18th and early 19th centuries.

Away from the turnpike roads, the same period saw a growth in bridge-building on local routes, notably in the upper Ouse valley, where Radwell, Felmersham and Oakley bridges replaced earlier fords. The development of the Ivel Navigation and the Grand Junction Canal in the late 18th and early 19th centuries also saw the construction of several bridges, most of which remained the responsibility of the Navigation and Canal operators.

THE COUNTY IN THE 19th CENTURY

By 1849, the County accepted responsibility (in whole or part) for 39 bridges.[24] Between 1868 and 1877 the Turnpike Trusts were wound up, and liability for their various bridges and culverts transferred to the County.[25] Enquiries were made in each parish as to which bridges were Turnpike bridges, and this is documented in detail in the Quarter Sessions Bridge Papers and Correspondence.

In 1881, the Higgins family off-loaded their responsibility for Turvey bridge on to the County. Attempts by various parishes to do the same with their bridges were unsuccessful: the Quarter Sessions decided that both Blunham and Langford bridges over the Ivel had been and still were repairable by their respective parish surveyors.

THE MODERN COUNTY COUNCIL

In 1888, in the first major local government reorganisation of modern times, the responsibilities of the Quarter Sessions for each county were transferred to newly created County Councils. In Bedfordshire, these responsibilities now included 190 bridges and culverts. A significant addition to existing powers and duties was the obligation to construct new bridges as well as to maintain existing ones.[26]

By 1893, the County Council had adopted a further 102 of the smaller privately maintained bridges built since 1803.[27] Between then and 1930 the remaining manorial bridges (Oakley, Stafford and Harrold) passed from private into public hands, with Sutton bridge following in 1941.

The minutes of the Highways and Bridges Committee of the County Council continued to note repairs to bridges,[28] but few detailed records survive from the late 19th and early 20th centuries. There are plans for the widening of Bromham bridge in 1902 and of Turvey bridge in 1930, and for the rebuilding of Stafford bridge in 1936, along with photographs of the work at Turvey and Stafford, but written documentation is largely missing until the 1950s. Since then records of individual structural surveys, underwater inspections, and repairs have been kept. At the time of writing[29] the County administers about 800 road bridges and culverts (including those on motorways and trunk roads, which are maintained on behalf of the Department of Transport).

NOTES

1   *Current Archaeology* 122, XI no 2, Nov 1990, 67, quoting *Antiquity* 64, 1990, 210-220

2   Excavations by Oxford Archaeological Unit in advance of construction of a rowing lake for Eton College, reported in *Current Archaeology* 148, June 1996, 124-127 and *British Archaeology* 9, Nov 1995, 5

3   D A Jackson & T M Ambrose, 'A Roman Timber Bridge at Aldwincle, Northamptonshire', *Britannia* 7, 1976, 39-72

4   R A Chambers, 'A Roman Timber Bridge at Ivy Farm, Fencott with Murcott, Oxon, 1979', *Oxoniensia* 51, 1986, 31-36

5   P T Bidwell and N Holbrook, *Hadrian's Wall Bridges,* English Heritage Archaeological Report 9, 1989, 67f & 348

6   F Stenton, *Anglo-Saxon England,* Oxford History of England, 3rd ed, 1971, 289-290; Webb & Webb, 1913, 86

7   Where not given in these notes, the detailed bibliographic references for Bedfordshire examples quoted in this section can be found under the individual bridges

8   B Durham *et al,* 'The Thames Crossing at Oxford: Archaeological Studies 1979-82', *Oxoniensia* 49, 1984, 57-100

9   G C Lee, *Leading Documents of English History,* 1900, 173

10 13 Edw I

11 Beds RO wills collection. Published examples can be found in *BHRS* 37, 1957; 44, 1966; 58, 1979

12 *BHRS* 45, 1966, 94 no 186

13 22 Hen VIII, c5; Webb & Webb, 1913, 89

14 27 Hen VIII, c28; 31 Hen VIII, c13; J D Mackie, *The Earlier Tudors,* Oxford History of England, 1985, 377 & 398

15 37 Hen VIII, c20; Webb & Webb, 1913, 399

16 See J E Brown, *Chantry Certificates for Bedfordshire,* nd, i

17 C Gorham, *History of St Neots,* 1820, 336-338

18 Beds RO: P 27/1/5. The document is undated but Lockgate I no 16, Jul 1965, 274 gives it as 'about 1630'

19 Beds RO: TW 841

20 Webb & Webb, 1913, 96

21 43 Geo III, c59; Webb & Webb, 1913, 101

22 Beds RO: QBM 1, 128-129

23 Godber, 1969, 316

24 Beds RO: QBM 1, 326-327

25 Godber, 1969, 517

26 51/52 Vic c21; Webb & Webb, 1913, 85; J J Clarke, *The Local Government of the United Kingdom (and the Irish Free State),* 1934, 296

27 Beds RO: QBP 9

28 Beds RO: Hi C M

29 Before April 1997, when Luton Borough Council becomes a unitary authority and takes responsibility for its own bridges

THE NENE VALLEY TRIBUTARIES

In the far north-west corner of Bedfordshire (the modern parishes of Podington and Wymington), the River Ise and its tributaries drain towards the River Nene in Northamptonshire (see Fig 6). They are small streams, not forming a major obstacle to communication. No documentary references to medieval bridges have been identified. The most notable surviving bridge is an 18th century stone structure at Hinwick; Podington bridge may have been of similar age but has been rebuilt.

HINWICK BRIDGE

HISTORY

Hinwick bridge[1] was built by Richard Orlebar of Hinwick House in 1779,[2] and carries the Podington-Wollaston road

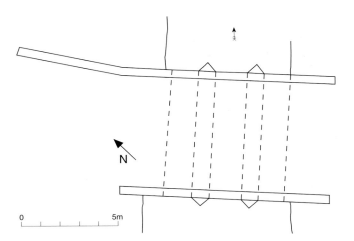

Fig 2 Hinwick bridge: ground plan

over a small stream. An earlier bridge is shown on the site on Jefferys' 1765 map of Bedfordshire. Very little is known about the bridge's subsequent history and the Orlebar family may not have taken responsibility for repairs after it was built. It was first repaired by the Quarter Sessions in 1842,[3] and formally adopted by the County Council after 1888.[4]

STRUCTURAL EVIDENCE

The bridge is a small structure of three arches, built in coursed squared rubble limestone. The central arch, 5 ft 3 in (1.6m) in width, is flanked by two smaller ones. The arch rings on both sides of the bridge have plain projecting keystones, but the voussoirs on the upstream (south) face are decorated by grooves incised into their faces. Double grooves extend right round the west and

Fig 3 Hinwick bridge: south face

central arches and the east side of the east arch. The remaining part of the east arch has only a single groove, perhaps reflecting a partial rebuild.

Irregular stepped half-pyramid cutwaters protect the narrow piers on both faces of the bridge. They rise to the height of the central arch crown. A series of carved heads project from both faces of the bridge, those on the south face being particularly fine. They appear to be medieval roof corbels, almost certainly reused from a church. Part of a carved stone panel, decorated with quatrefoil motif, has also been set into the inside face of the north parapet. The Orlebars had strong connections with local churches,[5] and it is possible that the corbels and stone panel were salvaged from a church restoration scheme.

The keystones at Hinwick, the decorative grooves on the arch rings and the projecting carved heads are unusual features for a remote country bridge. They are more at home on the elaborately designed classical-style park and town bridges of the period. These special features no doubt owe their origin to the bridge's association with the Orlebar family, and its location on the edge of their landscaped park.

Fig 4 Hinwick bridge: carved corbel on south face

14

NOTES
1 SP 935 621; HER 725
2 J Britton & E W Brayley, *The beauties of England and Wales*, vol 1, 1801, 79
3 Beds RO: QBM 1, 301
4 Beds RO: QBP 9
5 The family held the advowson of Podington church (*VCH Beds* 3, 1912, 87)

PODINGTON BRIDGE

Podington bridge[1] carries the Wymington road across the small River Ise at the north-east end of the village. Though now replaced with concrete arches, a sketch elevation in the Quarter Sessions bridge papers show that it was originally a three-arched stone bridge with half-pyramid cutwaters.[2] It was similar to Hinwick bridge, and was probably also of 18th century origin. In 1858, a new stone parapet replaced a decayed post and rail fence.[3]

NOTES
1 SP 942 627; HER 15733
2 Beds RO: QBP 10, 1873, p103
3 Beds RO: QBM 1, 396

THE OUSE VALLEY

The River Great Ouse is the most substantial watercourse in the county. It runs through a broad valley which, before the days of modern flood relief schemes, could be impassable for much of the winter because of floods. Ancient ford sites are recorded in placenames at Eaton Ford (St Neots), Little Barford, Tempsford, Great Barford, Bedford and Stafford (Oakley); they also existed at Clapham, Oakley, Radwell, Felmersham and Harrold, and no doubt many other local crossings were also utilised, particularly at times of low water. Watermill sites often had small bridges associated with them; the Domesday Book of 1086 records mills attached to all the parishes along the river, of which several have survived in some form into modern times. There is specific evidence of mill bridges at Castle Mills, Newnham, Kempston, Oakley and Sharnbrook.

These small local crossings were, however, inadequate for traffic on major highways, particularly during the winter months. It is no surprise therefore that the earliest, and the greatest, medieval bridges of the county were those in the Ouse valley. It may be that Bedford bridge was the first to be built, because of the strategic importance of the town in Saxon times. Bridges at St Neots, Harrold and Turvey are first documented in the 12th century, and Bromham in the early 13th, but there had almost certainly been bridges in those locations for some considerable time. There are no early references for Stafford bridge (in Oakley), but it was also medieval in origin.

The four great bridges of Willey Hundred (Bromham, Stafford, Harrold and Turvey) form a small but homogeneous group. Their histories display a complexity of

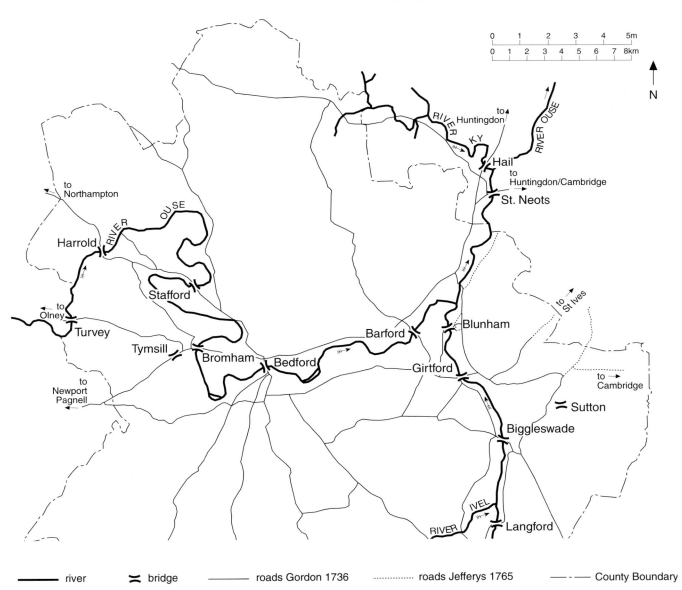

Fig 5 Medieval routes and bridges in the Ouse and Ivel valleys

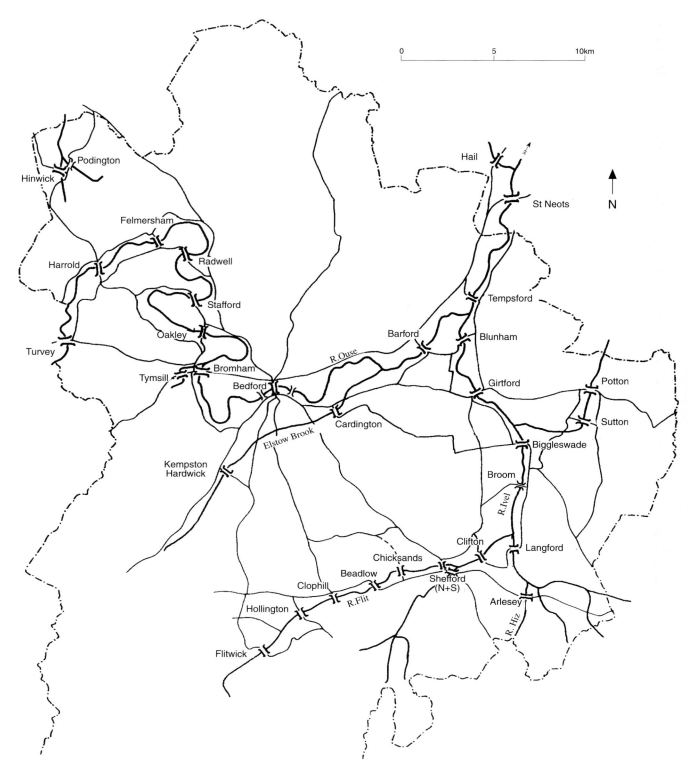

Fig 6 Location plan of bridges in the Ouse, Ivel and Flit valleys

manorial liabilities and organisation which is reflected in the very masonry of the individual bridges. They formed an integral part of the medieval road system in north Bedfordshire (Fig 5), connecting Bedford with other historic towns at Newport Pagnell, Olney and Northampton. As well as spanning the main river, they were also provided with long foot causeways (known locally as 'causeys') across the broad flood plain.

To the east of Bedford the road to Huntingdonshire crossed the Ouse at St Neots (also provided with a causeway) and only in c.1429 was a further crossing built at Great Barford. These gave enough bridging points (along with a few smaller bridges over tributary streams, such as Tymsill and Hail) until traffic grew in post-medieval times. The development of a network of turnpike trusts in the 18th century radically changed the communications pattern in the north of the county. In particular Harrold was by-passed whilst Bromham and, to a lesser extent, Turvey were 'improved'. In the case of Bromham a new road causeway was built on the site of the foot causeway, whilst at Turvey new arches were built on the Buckinghamshire side and the old causeway abandoned. Even the single arch at Tymsill on the Newport Pagnell turnpike displays several widenings. Growth in traffic on the Great North road resulted in the first bridge at Tempsford in 1736, replaced by the present stone structure in 1820.

New bridges were also constructed on local roads in the upper Ouse valley (Oakley, Radwell and Felmersham). These were very much in the local medieval tradition, but Cardington bridge, rebuilt in the 18th century by Samuel Whitbread, was designed by an architect of national renown, John Smeaton.

In Bedford itself, the medieval stone bridge was replaced by the fine neo-classical bridge in the early 19th century, and a new crossing was added in Prebend Street in 1883. The Suspension bridge was built in 1888 as part of the development of the Embankment and its associated landscaping.

HAIL BRIDGE, Eaton Socon

Below St Neots the Great Ouse is joined from the west by the River Kym. About a mile above the confluence the Great North road (A1) crosses the Kym at Hail bridge.[1] Now within Cambridgeshire, Hail bridge was partly administered by the Bedfordshire Quarter Sessions and later by Bedfordshire County Council until county boundary changes in 1964.

The bridge is first recorded in the Coroner's roll for 1265 as 'Hailebrugge'.[2] After an attempted robbery, 'the felons fled to Hail bridge below Sudbury on the boundary of Huntingdonshire and Bedfordshire, where William the Shepherd of Sir William of Sudbury joined the hue; and on the bridge John son of Richard Herebert struck him on the right side of his head with a fauchun [a falchion or sword], cutting off part of his head with the brain and right ear, so that he immediately died there.' A reference to 'Halyisbrigg' occurs in 1276 in the Hundred Rolls.[3]

Ogilby showed 'a wood bridg' at the site in the 17th century,[4] but this had been replaced in brick by 1828.[5] It had perhaps been rebuilt by the Biggleswade to Alconbury Hill Turnpike Trust, which is known to have carried out repairs.[6] Repairs are noted in Quarter Sessions records from 1828 onwards.[7] In 1888 it was recorded as having several brick arches,[8] but the site is now under the dual carriageway of the A1.

NOTES
1 TL 176 617
2 *BHRS* 41, 1961, 1 no 2
3 Mawer & Stenton, 1926, 264
4 Jervoise, 1932, 97; Beds RO: MC 2/51
5 Beds RO: QBM 1, 225
6 Beds RO: eg X 40/4, 17.3.1801
7 Beds RO: QBM 1, 219
8 Beds RO: QBP 9

ST NEOTS BRIDGE

A modern concrete bridge now spans the River Ouse at St Neots, occupying exactly the same site as a stone bridge demolished in 1963. The county boundary formerly ran down the centre of the main river channel, and the old bridge was jointly administered by Huntingdonshire and Bedfordshire until its demolition; Huntingdonshire was responsible for the eastern one and a half arches, Bedfordshire for the remaining thirteen and a half. The site now lies wholly within Cambridgeshire.[1]

THE MEDIEVAL TIMBER BRIDGE

There was probably a ford at St Neots, but a bridge known as the 'High bridge' had been built by 1180.[2] It is mentioned again in 1254 when William de Ferrers, the Earl of Derby, fell from his litter whilst being carried across the bridge. It seems that the Earl fell on dry land as 'his limbs were so shattered by the fall, that he survived only a short time, and died on 24th March'.[3]

Medieval records indicate some dispute as to who was liable for the bridge's maintenance. In 1294, Bishop Sutton of Lincoln granted '20 days' indulgence' (remission of punishment in purgatory) to those who contributed to the repair of the bridge.[4] In 1349 the tenants of the manor of Eaton, west of the river, made representations that the Prior of St Neots had not repaired the causeway.[5]

Permission to levy tolls ('pontage') was granted by Richard II in 1388 for two years to the bailiff and men of St Neots as the bridge was then in a ruinous state,[6] and in 1438 Roger Benethon bequeathed 3s 4d towards the bridge.[7] These were either in recognition that the Priory was not exclusively responsible for maintenance, or perhaps the Prior was failing to carry out his duties. The medieval bridge was evidently a timber structure as Leland, Henry VIII's antiquary, noted in the early 1530s that 'The Bridge of Seint Neotes is of Tymbar.'[8]

After the Dissolution of St Neots Priory in 1539, it is doubtful whether the new landowners inherited any obligation to repair the bridge. Inquiries in 1588 by Commissioners for Queen Elizabeth[9] found that anciently the Priory had been largely responsible for the bridge, but since the Suppression the inhabitants of St Neots and various well-disposed people in the neighbouring counties had maintained it.

The Queen's Commissioners described the bridge as 704 ft (214.6m) long, of which one section was 448 ft (135m) long and 10½ ft (3.2m) wide with 43 arches 'wholly built of timber'. The remainder of the bridge was 256 ft (78m) long and 7½ ft (2.3m) wide; this section had 29 timber arches of several heights, and of varying lengths of 7, 9 and 12 ft (2.1m, 2.7m and 3.7m), built upon a stone wall 6 ft (1.8m) high. (The 'arches' were presumably timber beams laid flat.)

Structural evidence

Remains of what must be assumed was the medieval bridge have been observed on two occasions. In 1906, five piers of an earlier bridge were seen beneath the river arches at low water. Each was 6 ft (1.8m) wide and consisted of a rubble core said to have been faced with Barnack stone, apparently with cutwaters on the down-stream face.[10] During construction of the present concrete bridge part of an old causeway was unearthed in the river bed whilst traces of piles and sleeper beams were found on the Bedfordshire bank.[11] No further information about any of these finds has been traced.

Of the two sections described in the 1588 survey it has been suggested that the stone causeway with 29 timber arches, 7½ ft (2.3m) wide, was the river bridge, while the timber structure of 43 arches, 10½ ft (3.2m) wide, carried the road across the flood plain.[12] However, the bridge carried an important road into the town and was unlikely to have had a wide approach over the flood plain with only a narrow 'packhorse' bridge leading into the town over the river (although there was just such an arrangement, albeit on a much larger scale, at the later bridge). Moreover, by plotting the lengths recorded by the Commissioners in 1588 against the topography of the floodplain, the length of the 10½ ft (3.2m) timber section matches the distance across the main river channels and the backwater. To the west the narrower causeway on a stone foundation crossed the higher ground of the flood plain. The medieval St Neots bridge was a typical Ouse valley bridge and causeway like Turvey, Harrold, Stafford or Bromham bridges (see below), except largely of wooden construction.

THE POST-MEDIEVAL STONE BRIDGE

Queen Elizabeth's Commissioners proposed that a new stone foundation with 44 arches be built, higher than the normal flood level. They instructed that the County of Bedfordshire (thereby establishing the County's subsequent liability) 'will frely cary to the repaire of the said Bridge 400 loades of lyme stone or other necessaries ...' and that 20 loads of timber should be taken from woods at Warden. Huntingdonshire was obliged to provide 153 tons of timber, whilst St Neots had to dig 276 loads of sand. Royal woods at 'Some'sham' in Cambridgeshire were to provide another 20 tons of wood and 'Diverse Persons therabouts have woods wherout 88 tonns of Timber may be taken'. A toll was to be raised to finance these works, which were to cost £575 12s 2d.[13]

It is not clear when this work began, but it was definitely in progress by 1609, when 200 tons of timber was felled in Bedfordshire,[14] probably for use in coffer dams, scaffolding and the wooden frameworks for constructing the arches. In 1616/17 over £1000 was collected for further work,[15] and some of the stone for the new bridge may have been derived from the ruins of the Priory.[16] Subsequent repairs were carried out by the County's Quarter Sessions, with a local Justice, Henry Ashley, being appointed Surveyor of the bridge in 1715.[17]

This stone bridge was demolished in 1963 without detailed recording; earlier drawings and photographs give some idea of its structural sequence (Fig 7), but it is not possible to date all the phases precisely.[18] A brief survey was published in 1925.[19]

Phase 1

The earliest identifiable parts of the bridge were the river arches (nos 1-3; Fig 8) with spans of 23 ft (7.0m), 50 ft 6 in (15.4m) and 36 ft 9 in (11.2m) respectively, and a carriageway of 10 ft 8 in (3.25m) at its widest point. The central arch (no 2) was particularly impressive, being quite the largest arch constructed over the River Ouse until engineering techniques improved in the late 18th and 19th centuries. Arches 2 and 3 were the most elaborate with chamfered ribbing connected by cross ribbing, which Jervoise noted as quite an unusual feature.[20] There were five vertical ribs at arch 3 but only four at arch 2, reflecting the relative narrowness of the central arch (Figs 9 and 10). The main span of arch 2 is narrower than its springing, which was originally intended to take a wider arch. In contrast to arches 2 and 3, arch 1 was very plain with a single order voussoir ring and little or no chamfer. It is identical in character to the first four flood arches (4 to 7), which must be broadly contemporary. The river arches and flood arches are separated by piers with pointed cutwaters both upstream and down, and the spandrels are in ashlar limestone.

Despite variations in design, arches 1 to 7 belong to one broad phase of construction. Assuming that one arch was formed at a time, in keeping with medieval methods, a construction sequence can be proposed. The earliest

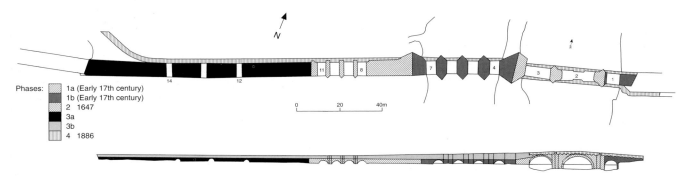

Fig 7 St Neots bridge: phase plan and elevation

arches (2 and 3) were the most decorative. Arch 3, 14 ft 5 in (4.40m) wide, had been completed and work was underway on the piers to arch 2, but at this stage there was a change: the arch sat awkwardly on its springing and the width narrowed to only 10 ft 8 in (3.25m), little wider than the earlier timber bridge. Dwindling finances seem the most ready explanation for this change in design, as the remaining arches were consistently plainer.

In 1645, during the Civil War, Parliament instructed that drawbridges be created at St Neots, Huntingdon and St Ives bridges.[21] If this order was carried out, it is possible that the easternmost arch (arch 1) was removed for a time, and subsequently replaced. This is another possible explanation for its different character.

Phase 2

West of arch 7 there was a long stretch of raised causeway leading to a second series of four rounded arches (8 to 11; Fig 11); these carried a broader roadway, approximately 22 ft (6.70m) wide. They were separated by a series of triangular cutwaters facing upstream but with flat pedestal buttresses on the downstream face. That between arches 9 and 10 bore an inscribed panel:-

A   N

1647

N   O

providing a *terminus ante quem* for the construction. The arches had a double arch ring with a slightly recessed

Fig 8 St Neots bridge: arches 1-3, north face (Co Engineer)

Fig 9 St Neots bridge: arch 2 ribbing (Co Engineer)

Fig 11 St Neots bridge: causeway arches 8 and 9, north face (Co Engineer)

lower order. The upper order of voussoirs was formed by ashlar limestone blocks two to three times the length of the lower order, which is not a common feature.

Phase 3a

Still further west, the tail end of the causeway was punctured by three small rounded arches (12 to 14) with a

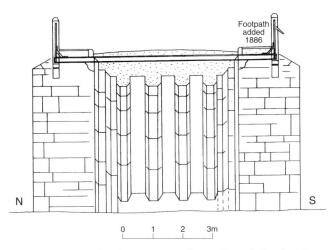

Fig 10 St Neots bridge: section through arch 2, showing ribbing

single order of ashlar limestone voussoirs. There were no cutwaters on either face, and there is brick instead of stone in much of the spandrel walls. A fifteenth arch was later added on the approach from Kimbolton, making the whole bridge a total of 794 ft (242m) long. The flood arches were mostly between 21 ft 8 in (6.6m) and 22 ft 4 in (6.8m) wide, tapering to only 20 ft (6.1m) by arch 14 at the west end.

Phase 3b

At some stage the overall height of the carriageway along the floodplain was raised, lessening the ramped approach to the river bridge. The heightening was faced in brick, though much of the brickwork was obscured by a stucco finish imitating the ashlar below. This work may date from after 1823, when the Rev Thomas Orlebar Marsh recorded extensive flood damage: '... the water was nearly 2 feet above the Crown of the Bridge ... About 100 yards of bridge wall at Eaton Ford was carried away ... Part of the parapet of the great bridge has been forced down, and the arch of the small Bridge leading from thence towards the North road blown up'.[22]

Phase 4

The bridge was widened in 1886 to create a footpath along the entire length of its north side, and also along the south side of the main river bridge.[23] This was supported on iron beams which rested on cantilevers tied into the face of the bridge.

THE MODERN BRIDGE

In 1963 the stone bridge and causeway were demolished and replaced by a concrete bridge, comprising a series of concrete beams supported on V-shaped legs. The approach viaduct is carried on columns broken up by rectangular concrete boxes faced in Weldon stone. The footpaths are cantilevered out from the face and clad in Clipsham limestone.

NOTES
1 TL 181 602; Cambs SMR ref 545; see also *Lockgate* I no 14, Jan 1965, 237-244
2 *Lockgate, op cit,* 237; *VCH Hunts* 2, 1932, 337
3 G C Gorham, *The History and Antiquities of Eynesbury and St Neots in Huntingdonshire,* 1820, 141-142; *Lockgate, op cit,* 238; R Young, 'St Neots bridge', *St Neots Local History Mag,* Summer 1963, 16-17
4 *Lincs Record Society* 52, 1958, 188
5 Gorham, *op cit,* 336
6 *Cal Patent Rolls* 1385-9, 479; Gorham, *op cit,* 142
7 *BHRS* 4, 1917, 1-3
8 L Toulmin Smith (ed), *John Leland's Itinerary in England and Wales* vol 1, 1964, 1
9 Gorham C, *op cit,* 142, 336-338
10 *ibid*
11 C F Tebbutt, *St Neots,* 1984, 204
12 Poulton A L H, 'New viaduct and bridge at St Neots', *Lockgate* I no 14, Jan 1965, 226-228
13 *Lockgate* I no 14, Jan 1965, 237-244
14 *Cal State Papers Dom* 1603-10, 492
15 *Cal State Papers Dom* 1611-18, 413, 441
16 Gorham, *op cit,* 142
17 Beds RO: QSM 2, 1715, 151
18 Photographs held by Co Engineer's Dept, Beds CC; Beds RO: PB 8, plans & elevations; Cambs RO (Huntingdon office): PH69C/1; PH69C/116/1-5
19 RCHME, *Huntingdonshire,* 1926, 224 and pl 24
20 Jervoise, 1932, 97
21 *VCH Hunts* 2, 1932, 338; *Lockgate* I no 14, Jan 1965, 238
22 Beds RO: BC 532, quoting *Huntingdon, Bedford & Peterborough Gazette,* Nov 8, Nov 15 & Dec 29, 1823
23 Beds RO: QSM 47, 1886, 705; 48, 1886, 48

TEMPSFORD BRIDGE

Architecturally perhaps the finest bridge in the county after Wing's bridge in Bedford, Tempsford is also the busiest. Before road improvements in the early 1960s it carried both lanes of the A1; it still carries all northbound traffic. Despite the present importance of the crossing, the first proposal for a bridge at Tempsford was not made until 1725.[1]

PHASE 1: FORD

Placename evidence suggests that Tempsford was already an important crossing by the early 10th century. The meaning of 'Taemeseford' is disputed: Mawer and Stenton suggested that this stretch of the Ouse was once known as the Thames;[2] Ekwall favoured the 'ford on the road to the Thames' (ie to London).[3] The settlement near the ford is still known as Langford End. References to a 'stonebrigge'[4] and Bulls bridge[5] in Tempsford in the 15th and 16th centuries probably refer to bridges on the Little Barford road and Mossbury Manor road respectively.

In the early 17th century, lighters (river barges) sailed only as far as Great Barford, but following an Act of Parliament in 1675,[6] the Ouse was opened up for navigation to Bedford, and river traffic greatly increased. The Tempsford ford across the shallows in the river became almost impassable for boatmen in the summer. One Francis Lord had to travel from Tempsford to Bromham to persuade the millers to let out their water in order to float his boats over Tempsford ford.[7] As a solution Henry Ashley, Undertaker to the Ouse Navigation, constructed a staunch below the ford which retained sufficient water to enable boats to pass.[8] In so doing neighbouring land was often flooded and the ford became more and more difficult to cross. Conflicting interests deepened when the Biggleswade to Alconbury Hill Turnpike Trust was established in 1725.[9] The Trustees were empowered to improve the road, and amongst their first resolutions was to construct a bridge at Tempsford.[10] In the meantime traffic continued to use the ford.

PHASE 2: TIMBER BRIDGE[11]

Despite private offers to finance or even build a bridge,[12] no action was taken until a Turnpike Renewal Act of 1736.[13] This enabled the Commissioners to raise some capital, and banned operation of the staunch between

Fig 12 Tempsford bridge: water-colour by Thomas Fisher, showing timber and stone bridges (Beds Record Office: X 67/934/60)

4 am and 8 pm until the bridge should be completed. After consideration of various tenders the Trustees selected a scheme by Thomas and Edward Franks for a six-arch timber bridge for £430.[14] The oak and fir bridge was built well to the north of the troublesome staunch and completed by late summer of 1736.[15] A new road to the bridge from the ford ran alongside the hauling path of the navigation. Under a further Renewal Act of 1770,[16] the Trustees had this approach road raised on a causeway which was punctured by three flood arches.

A further 21-year lease was granted to the Trustees in 1791,[17] when repairs to the bridge were recorded by Viscount Torrington:

'Tempsford bridge is now repairing, idly with wood, instead of being well built with stone which such a road demands, and the Turnpike Trust could well afford; so I was obliged to cross the ford at Wroxton, which had not the water been let down had been impossible for Poney'.[18]

Nothing is known of the structure of the timber bridge, although a general impression is given in a drawing by Thomas Fisher (Fig 12).[19]

PHASE 3: STONE BRIDGE[20]

By 1814, responsibility for the bridge had passed to the Quarter Sessions, and in that year John Wing reported that the wooden structure was unsafe.[21] He recommended that it should be replaced by a stone bridge of three arches in Sandy stone, with seven flood arches some 70 to 80 yards (64-73m) to the west, for £17,850. Plans drawn up by Robert Salmon matching these requirements survive in the Bedfordshire Record Office.[22] The Quarter Sessions obtained an Act of Parliament to rebuild the bridge, the finance being raised through rates and tolls.[23] A plan by Thomas Lilburne, attached to the Act, showed the proposed new bridge and causeway in relation to the ford and the timber bridge (Fig 13). The Quarter Sessions invited Wing to draw up an alternative scheme and asked Lilburne to design the approach road and flood bridges. Evidently their proposals (for a river bridge of three arches in Ketton stone for £15,090, and flood arches and roadway for £6155) proved too expensive.[24] The Quarter Sessions therefore advertised for alternative designs and accepted a proposal estimated at £7300 from James Savage,[25] a noted architect of road bridges in the early 19th century.[26]

In 1815 agreement was reached with William Allen of London to construct Savage's bridge for £9550, to be paid in eight instalments.[27] The lengthy draft articles of agreement are preserved in the Bedfordshire Record Office, along with Savage's plans and elevation drawings.[28] These meticulous specifications can be usefully

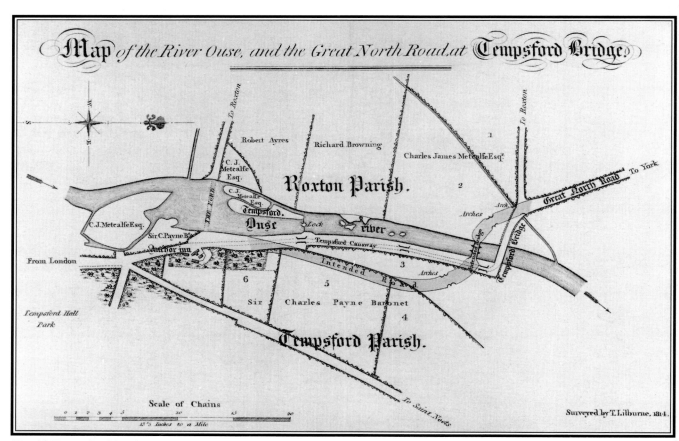

Fig 13 Tempsford bridge: plan by Thomas Lilburne, 1814, showing the site of the proposed stone bridge (Beds Record Office: Z 417/29)

compared with the completed bridge, and give details of the otherwise hidden foundations.

There seem to have been problems from the outset. In July 1816, Allen had to assure Theed Pearse (the Clerk to the Justices of the Peace) that he had used beech piles in the foundations and not fir.[29] By October 1816 Allen was behind in the work and the Quarter Sessions withheld the fourth instalment. Pearse visited the site on 20th September 1817 with the architect, James Savage, and found that work had hardly progressed. He found the same dam as the previous year, one pier and one abutment pier nearly up, but no other work on the main bridge begun. The piers of the Roxton flood arches were up but the arches had not been turned (though the centres were being prepared).[30]

Work to the approaches on the Tempsford bank was also delayed, due to a dispute over the selected route. On Lilburne's plan the new road was to lie immediately east of the earlier road, but the builders were following a more easterly route (on the line of the present northbound carriageway of the A1). The landowner objected, but the

Quarter Sessions agreed to buy the land in question and work was able to recommence.[31]

By 1818, the disagreements between contractor and architect were becoming increasingly acrimonious. For example, Allen complained that Savage had instructed him to build the piers in rubble like Girtford or Blunham, but had told the Quarter Sessions that the work would be done in masonry.[32] (The contract, to which Allen had agreed, clearly specified ashlar).[33] Work came to a halt as the dispute dragged on, but eventually a new contract was awarded in February 1819 to a Mr Johnson.[34] The new builder adhered to the original specification, except for requesting that Bramley Fall stone (quarried near Leeds) be used for the arch soffits as well as the voussoirs, as he could not procure sufficient adequate stone from Sandy in a reasonable time.[35] He also asked to use 14 inch brickwork in the flood arches instead of 12 inch stonework. Finally on 18th October 1820, the bridge was certified as complete.[36]

Since 1820 the bridge has been repaired through the Quarter Sessions and from 1888 by its successor, the County Council. Major repairs were carried out in 1994.

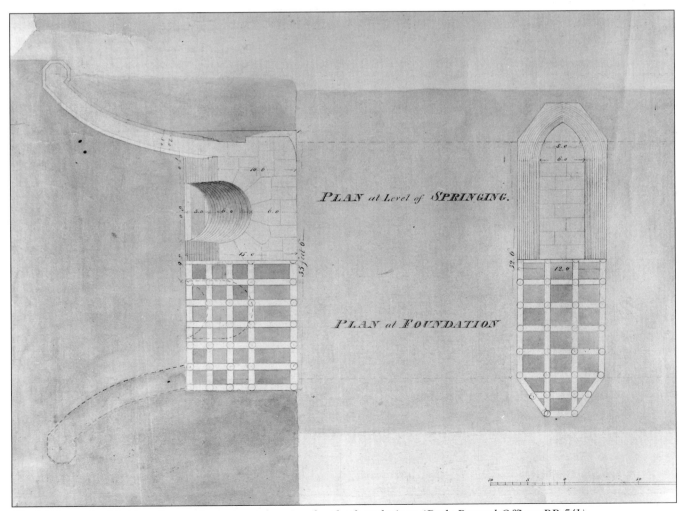

Fig 14 Tempsford bridge: Savage's contract drawing for the foundations (Beds Record Office: PB 5/1)

Fig 15 Tempsford bridge: south face of river bridge (Beds Photographic Services)

Structural evidence

The River Bridge

The bridge remains remarkably unaltered since completion in 1820, apart from the all too frequent accident damage to the sandstone parapets.

The nature of the foundations is known only from Savage's original written specifications and drawings (see Fig 14). The piers were to rest upon a timber foundation set 3 ft (0.91m) below the river bed. This comprised a grating supported by a series of vertically driven bearing piles. Savage instructed that the foundations were to be piled using sound elm or beech or other suitably strong timber. (If Allen used fir as alleged, this may have weakened the superstructure, causing the cracking which has been a continual problem in the west abutment.) Each pile was to have a 9 inch (230mm) upper diameter and to be as long as to reach into firm ground, with a shoe of wrought iron. The heads of each pile were to be levelled and capped with four longitudinal sleepers under each pier and five under each abutment, with thirteen cross sleepers. The voids in the grating were to be infilled with rammed stone to form a level building platform. Above this foundation, the piers were of solid stone up to the arch springing; this part of the construction was confirmed during repairs in 1994, when the fill over the towpath arch and adjacent pier was removed.

The piers were to be 12 ft (3.7m) wide at the base reducing in a curve to only 6 ft (1.8m) at the arch springing. Stonework in the abutments was gradually stepped back, forming two 'arches' in the core of each abutment in order to lock the bridge to the causeway.

The river span (Fig 15) is typical of many later 18th and early 19th century masonry bridges. There are three broad low segmental arches, solidly built from massive blocks of Bramley Fall stone. The voussoirs are cleverly shaped, with a broad curved chamfer gradually tapering out by the single projecting keystone (Fig 16). Ruddock likened this feature to *cornes de vache* (cow's horns) seen on some French bridges, eg *Pont de Neuilly* (1776), but it does not seem to be a common feature on British bridges.[37] They were part of James Black's unexecuted design for rebuilding London bridge around 1800, but the first bridge to use them was at Ringsend on the River Dodder, at Dublin in 1803.[38] Tempsford would seem to be the first English bridge where they appear, though they were more successfully executed by Alexander Nimmo on Wellesley (Sarsfield) bridge, Limerick (1824- 35), and by Thomas Telford on Over bridge, Gloucester (1826-30) and at Morpeth (1831).[39]

Such a feature gave a hydraulic benefit, allowing water to pass more easily than through a sharp-edged opening.[40] The piers at Tempsford, gradually broadening in a smooth

Fig 16 Tempsford bridge: detail of voussoirs and cutwater (Beds Photographic Services)

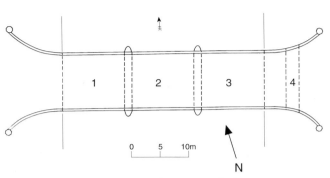

Fig 18 Tempsford river bridge: ground plan

curve, display similar properties. Like the chamfer they also seem to be a poor copy of the features at Ringsend bridge where the *cornes de vache* return via the abutments to form a solid invert.

In typical 18th or 19th century fashion, the cutwaters rise to the arch springing, and they are faced and capped in Bramley Fall stone. The rather elaborate capstones are cleverly shaped to angle flood water through the arches with the least resistance.

Given the careful attention to the arch shape and pier design the abutments are disappointingly square by comparison, but they do incorporate Bramley Fall stone on their most exposed angle up to springing level. The east abutment is punctured by the rounded towpath arch, provided for the navigation. Unlike the river arches it has a brick soffit faced with large sandstone voussoirs.

The bridge has a solid sandstone parapet, which includes some massive blocks, resting on a projecting Bramley Fall stone string course. The line of the parapets is broken by slightly projecting fascias or panels over the piers and keystones of the arches, though several of these have been removed in repairs following accident damage. The projections are repeated on the string course, which rests directly on the keystones. The wing walls, string course and parapet finish in large octagonal terminals. Bramley Fall stone copings run the length of the bridge, except where they have been replaced in concrete. They are gradually tapered, decreasing in width towards the terminals.

Inscriptions of masons who worked on the bridge survive on the inside face of the copings over the crown of the centre arch. That on the south parapet reads 'T Toller 1820'; 'M George 1820' and 'C N' are recorded on the

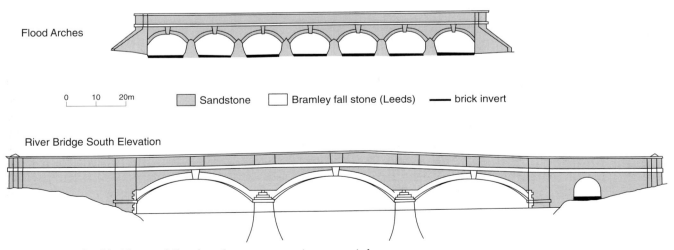

Fig 17 Tempsford bridge and flood arches: construction materials

north parapet. On the external face of the bridge, the upstream (south) string course carries the following:-
J. SAVAGE. ARCHITECT. 1820. JOHNSON. & SON. BUILDERS.
There is no mention of Allen, the original builder.

During resurfacing work in 1994, massive concrete blocks (cubes of about 1.0m), each with a socket in the upper face, were uncovered at the east end of the river bridge. These were the remains of a Second World War bridge defence system.

The Flood Arches
Separated from the river bridge by short stretches of contemporary embankment, the two sets of seven flood arches are almost identical to each other. The small segmental arches are in brick, faced with sandstone voussoirs; each has a disproportionately large, raised, projecting keystone. The piers have keeled half-pyramid cutwaters rising to the arch springing on both elevations. Unlike the river bridge there are angled abutments on both upstream and downstream faces, partly to direct the water flow, but also to retain the embankment. The floors are protected by flat brick inverts laid along the long axis of the arch.

The flood arches have a broad plain projecting string course in Bramley Fall stone, with a plain stone parapet, also capped in Fall stone. The parapets finish in octagonal terminals. On the west (Roxton) bank there was a single culvert immediately beyond the flood arches; this is the only part of the original construction not to survive, having been replaced in concrete.

NOTES
1   See also Peter McKeague, 'Tempsford Bridge', *Beds Mag*, 22 no 170, Autumn 1989, 72-75; *Lockgate* I no 10, Jan 1964, 160-163; no 11, Apr 1964, 177-181; no 12, Jul 1964, 190-194; no 13, Oct 1964, 210-213
2   Mawer & Stenton, 1926, 111
3   E Ekwall, *The Concise Oxford Dictionary of English Place-Names*, Oxford Clarendon Press, 2nd ed, 1940, 441
4   Beds RO: BS 1283 (1465)
5   Beds RO: BS 658 (1556)
6   16/17 Chas II c12; D Summers, *The Great Ouse: The History of a River Navigation*, 1973, 50
7   *BHRS* 24, 1946, 24
8   *BHRS* 24, 1946, 71
9   11 Geo I c20 (copy in Beds RO: Z 417/26); *BHRS Survey of Ancient Buildings* 3, 1926, 11-12
10 Beds RO: X 261, p3 (the Minute Book of the Biggleswade-Alconbury Turnpike Trust)
11 TL 163 547; HER 15758
12 Beds RO: X 261, p45 (1726) – Mr Ashley proposed to lend money to build a bridge; p74 (1728) – Thomas and Edward Franks of Eaton offered to build an oak bridge
13 *BHRS Survey of Ancient Buildings* 3, 1926, 12
14 Beds RO: X 261, p147
15 Beds RO: X 261, pp156-7; *Lockgate* I no 10, Jan 1964, 161
16 *BHRS Survey of Ancient Buildings* 3, 1926, 12
17 *ibid*
18 Andrews C Bruyn, *The Torrington Diaries*, vol 2, 1935, 316
19 Beds RO: X 67/934/60
20 TL 162 545; HER 5994
21 Beds RO: QBM 1, 68
22 Beds RO: PB 5/5-6
23 55 George III c30 (copy in Beds RO: Z 417/29); see also QBM 1, 69-70 (1814)
24 Beds RO: QBM 1, 71, 73
25 Beds RO: QBP 8/1
26 Ruddock, 1979, 196
27 Beds RO: QBP 8/4
28 Beds RO: QBP 8/3, 8/7; PB 5/1-4
29 Beds RO: H/WS 1489, 19.7.1816
30 Beds RO: H/WS 1489, 20.9.1817
31 Beds RO: QBP 8/1
32 Beds RO: H/WS 1489, 26.1.1818
33 Beds RO: PB 8/3
34 Beds RO: H/WS 1489, 8.2.1819
35 Beds RO: H/WS 1489, 18.8.1819; H/WS 1248, 26.8.1819. A similar situation was encountered during the 1994 repairs. While sand quarries on Sandy Heath regularly produce large blocks of sandstone which match the texture and colour of the original stonework exactly, they are usually full of sand pockets and other weaknesses. Stone from quarries near Leighton Buzzard was therefore substituted.
36 Beds RO: QBM 1, 127
37 Ruddock, 1979, 196
38 *ibid*, 177
39 *ibid*, 233-243
40 *ibid*, 176-7

BARFORD BRIDGE

Barford bridge connects Blunham and Great Barford parishes, and is the nearest public road crossing of the Great Ouse downstream of Bedford.[1] Extensive repairs were undertaken by the County Surveyor between 1982 and 1990.

PHASE 1 – THE 15th CENTURY BRIDGE

'I wol that the briyge of Berford in Bedfordshyr be perfourmed and finished with my goods.'

The history of Barford bridge begins with this codicil to the will of Sir Gerard Braybroke of Colmworth, in 1427/29.[2] It is clear that this bequest was for the construction of a new bridge rather than the repair of an existing one because in 1447 the inhabitants of Bedford complained that the new bridge at Barford was drawing traffic away from Bedford to other market towns; as a result the town was impoverished and could not pay its rents due to the Crown.[3]

The bridge as first built consisted only of eight arches across the river. John Leland described it in the 1530s as 'a great stone bridge of eight stone arches near the uplandisch towne of Berford'.[4] These are arches 8 to 15 of the present bridge (see Figs 19 and 21).

Although some of the arches have since been rebuilt,

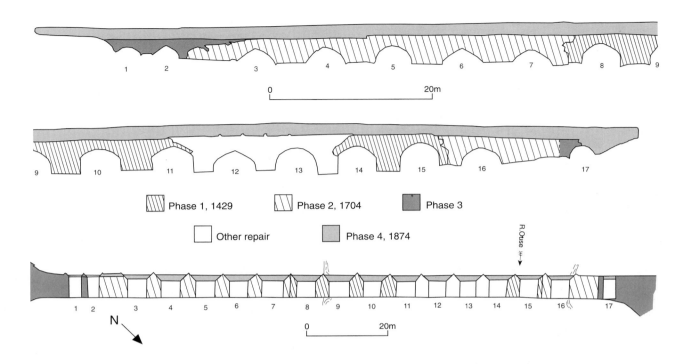

Phase 1, 1429   Phase 2, 1704   Phase 3

Other repair   Phase 4, 1874

R.Ouse →

Downstream (East) Elevation & Ground Plan

Fig 19 Barford bridge: phase plan and elevation

enough remains to reconstruct what the late medieval bridge may have looked like. The south end of the original bridge can be identified by the abrupt change in stone type and coursing on the south bank at pier 7/8 (Fig 20), and on the north bank by a change in the coursing of the limestone rubble at pier 15/16. Now standing in the river channel this pier once formed the north abutment; the north bank of the river has since receded, perhaps altered during 17th century improvements to the Ouse navigation.[5]

Although the original bridge has been repaired many

times, it seems that the pier bases, abutments, arch soffits and, possibly, cutwaters were in sandstone whilst the remainder was in rubble limestone. There was a moulded limestone string course; where it survives, its chamfered upper surface and moulded lower face suggest that it dates from the 15th century. Only part of the original line of the string course survives (Fig 21), extending over the crown of the arches but dropping at pier 7/8 (the original south abutment), at pier 9/10, over arch 12 (which has been rebuilt), and formerly at the original northern abutment. Perhaps the string course was originally much more

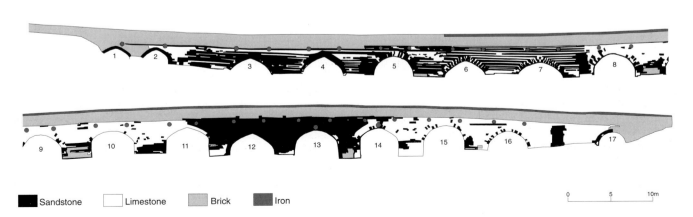

Sandstone   Limestone   Brick   Iron

Fig 20 Barford bridge: construction materials, east elevation

Fig 21 Barford bridge: east face of main river bridge (arch 10 in foreground) (Beds Photographic Services)

symmetrical, dropping at the abutments and then at every other pier.

After it was built, Barford bridge benefited from several bequests towards repairs. In 1501, John Canon of Great Barford left 6s 8d (an angel) 'to the repairs of Barford bridge'[6] and Edward Cowper of Blunham left 2 shillings.[7] Five years later a Blunham resident Richard Manley also left an angel to the bridge.[8] In 1534, Richard Wylshire left a quarter of malt to the 'reparacyions',[9] and the next year John Fitzgeffery, lord of Creakers manor in Barford, left ten quarters of barley.[10]

Among the documents of the Cranfield family of Great Barford is a set of 16th century accounts for repairs.[11] One payment referred to 'creast [crest] stones which was taken owt of the water and ... mending the toppe of the bridge with lyme and stone that was left'. There was possibly also some work to the foundations: 'viij [8] dayes workes digging gravel and earth about the arches and bottom of the bridge.' Stone was transported from Biddenham (limestone) and Sandy (sandstone).

In spite of this history of private maintenance, the County undertook repairs in 1651[12] and was found liable for the bridge at the assizes in 1671.[13]

PHASE 2 – THE FLOOD ARCHES

In the late 17th/early 18th century, five arches (3 to 7) were added over the low flood plain on the south side of the river. The junction between the old and new work is clearly marked by a change in the style of construction

and by an offset joint on the east face. This face was elaborately built using alternating bands of sandstone and limestone (Fig 22), which may be a design of local inspiration copying the stonework of the Norman arches in Blunham church. The effect is still very clear despite numerous repairs. A datestone built into pier 6/7 bears the initials 'W.S.' and the date '1704', probably recording the construction of this phase (the identity of 'W.S.' is unknown).

The arches consisted of two orders of alternating limestone and sandstone voussoirs forming a chequerboard pattern, though all of them, apart from arches 6 and 7,

Fig 22 Barford bridge: east face of flood arches (arch 4 in foreground)

have been repaired in sandstone. They are generally four-centred, an unusual form of arch construction in the early 18th century. Although it is now masked by later work, the west face seems to have been built purely in sandstone. Above there was a simple triangular string course, partly of limestone and partly of sandstone.

The south end of this phase can be identified by the steeply inclined coursing of the large pier 2/3 on the west face, showing that this originally served as the south abutment, carrying the road by a ramp on to the bridge (Fig 23). This feature is not visible in the banded work on the east elevation which has been partly refaced.

There was a similar though much shorter extension to the northern end of the bridge. One arch (no 16) and a new abutment were added. Although little of the original coursing and stonework now survives, the character of this work matches the southern extension. The arch is four-centred and the pier very similar to the south abutment at pier 2/3. Photographs of the original stonework before repairs in 1982 show that the east face of pier 16/17 was of massive coursed sandstone construction with a steeply inclined upper course rising on to the bridge.[14]

From the late 17th century onwards there are frequent references in the Quarter Sessions minutes and in other local records to the need for repairs. In 1753 part of arch 5 collapsed and it was repaired with (lime)stone from Harrold and Pavenham.[15] The date was inscribed into the keystone on the east face but is now barely visible. The rebuilt arch has a rounded profile in contrast to the pointed arches either side.

PHASE 3 – 18th CENTURY ALTERATIONS

Sometime in the 18th century, the bridge was further extended by the addition of a rounded arch (arch 17) to the north end, and arches 1 and 2 (simple single order pointed arches) to the south end. At the south abutment, the approach ramp was levelled up and new quoins inserted at the south end to tie in with the new arch 2.[16]

After 1772, when the road across the bridge was turn-piked,[17] a new road towards Roxton was laid out from its north-east corner. Vehicles had difficulty turning through the sharp angle and the Quarter Sessions minutes for 1776 record that the road was a nuisance.[18] A narrow brick widening was therefore added to the east face of the north abutment to lessen this angle for traffic.

Fig 23 Barford bridge: west face, showing the brick widening of 1873. The sloping courses in the sandstone pier (foreground) mark the south end of phase 2 of the bridge (Beds Photographic Services)

More work to the bridge was carried out by John Wing in 1781, when two of the original eight arches (12 and 13) seem to have been rebuilt. Wing was paid £85 12s 10d, and the items of expenditure included stone from Sandy and elm scantling to form centring for constructing arches.[19] The character of the new stonework is very similar to that at Girtford bridge, which he built in the same year.

In 1794, the bridge is described by Viscount Torrington as having seventeen arches and being very narrow.[20] An early 19th century watercolour by Thomas Fisher also shows the bridge at its present length, with stone parapets along the whole bridge.[21]

PHASE 4 – 19th CENTURY WIDENING

By 1817 traffic was so heavy that plans were drawn up for widening the bridge 'by throwing proper timber beams from pier to pier well fastened down to wall plates and guarded by three rails and by covering the same with three inch oak plank ... '. This work to the west elevation was completed in 1818, increasing the width of the carriage-way from 12 ft (3.7m) to 16 ft (4.9m). The solid parapet along the west side of the bridge was removed and replaced by an open railing.[22] A few years later the east parapet was also replaced by a wooden one.

Towards the end of 1823 the bridge was badly damaged by flood.[23] The south-east corner collapsed and was rebuilt, and two damaged arches and a fence wall needed to be repaired. This work can be seen in the east spandrels of arches 1 and 2 which have been refaced, first in rubble limestone, then in brick. The limestone walling may be the 1824 repair.

Several of the voussoirs in arch 1 and other arches of the bridge have been replaced by monolithic sandstone slabs with the bedding plane running parallel with the arch ring, contrary to the laws of arch building. These too are probably 19th century repairs.

Following the collapse of an iron bridge at Broom under the weight of a traction engine in 1873, the County Surveyor was obliged to examine the strength of other bridges in the county.[24] As a result of this, the decaying timber widening was replaced in 1874. The initial intention was to use iron girders stretched from pier to pier, but instead an elaborate brick skin was built over the length of the bridge along its west side.[25] Most of the medieval stonework along that face has been obscured as a result. Only the tips of the cutwaters, the arch rings and surrounding spandrels, and the pier bases remain visible. The pointed brickwork arches were decorated by brick 'voussoirs' in three orders with every alternate brick left out, creating a 'missing cog' appearance (Fig 23).

Brick parapets were added along both sides of the bridge, with small brick buttresses every 13 ft (4.0m) along the external face. On the west (upstream) side the cutwaters were extended up to the parapets in brick. The whole parapet may originally have been completely capped in iron copings, but only a few now survive on the east side. There are at least two varieties of coping, some cast by Barwell and Co, Northampton. Each joint is individually numbered with Roman numerals incised into the crest of the copings and infilled with a white inlay. The rest of the copings on the bridge are blue half-round bricks.

The widening was not a structural success. After some twenty years the brick face was separating from the stonework behind; it had never been securely tied in, and the void between the stone and brick faces had simply been infilled with debris and earth. In 1897, massive iron tie-bars, made by Baker and Co of Bedford, were inserted at regular intervals along the length of the bridge to restrain the walls.[26] Even so there are areas where this has not prevented further movement and part of the walls between the tie-bars have pushed out still further.

NOTES
1   TL 134 516; HER 996; see also Peter McKeague, 'Great Barford Bridge', *Beds Mag* 21 no 163, Winter 1987, 97-99; Bedfordshire County Planning Department's *'Discovering our Past' Broadsheet Series* no 12, 'Barford Bridge', Peter McKeague, 1989; *Lockgate* I no 8, Jul 1963, 128-132; no 9, Oct 1963, 138-140
2   *BHRS* 2, 1914, 41-43
3   W Henman, 'Bedford Bridge and its Story', *Beds Times,* 31 Oct 1913; *VCH Beds* 1, 1912, 3
4   Toulmin Smith L (ed), *John Leland's Itinerary in England & Wales,* London, vol 4, 1964, 22
5   Godber, 1969, 320
6   *BHRS* 58, 1979, 52-53 no 58
7   *BHRS* 45, 31 no 66
8   *BHRS* 57, 1979, 77 no 61
9   Beds RO: ABP/R 4 f3d
10 Beds RO: ABP/R 4 f34d
11 Beds RO: X 80/97
12 Beds RO: TW 841
13 Beds RO: HSA 1672 S7
14 In HER
15 Beds RO: FN 1253, 81-85
16 This work is not specifically recorded in the Quarter Sessions records, though the substantial sum of £70 was paid for 'repairs' in 1753 (Beds RO: QBM 1, 13)
17 *BHRS Survey of Ancient Buildings* 3, 1936, 20
18 Beds RO: QBM 1, 22
19 Beds RO: QBM 1, 25; QSR 14, 1781, 161
20 Andrews C Bruyn (ed), *The Torrington Diaries,* 1938, vol 4, 62
21 Beds RO: slide 129, from an original at Bedford Town Hall, nd
22 Beds RO: QBM 1, 102-3; QSR 23, 1817, 474; 24, 1819, 406
23 Beds RO: BC 532, T O Marsh papers; QSR 26, 1824, 496
24 Beds RO: QBC 5; QBP 4
25 Beds RO: QBC 5
26 Beds RO: Hi C M 3, p138

CARDINGTON BRIDGE

HISTORY

Deeds mention a bridge at Cardington in 1697/8,[1] and a map of the Cardington estate of Elizabeth Whitbread, 1765, shows two bridges on the site of the present bridge.[2] The more westerly carried the road north from Cardington village towards Bedford. Samuel Whitbread engaged John Smeaton, a noted architect, to build a new bridge on this site in 1778; his original drawings survive in the Library of the Royal Society.[3]

Fig 24 Cardington bridge: west face

The County repaired a 'Cardington bridge' in 1818,[4] but this was probably a bridge on the Barford road to the north-east. Smeaton's bridge seems to have been formally adopted only after the creation of the County Council in 1888.[5] It had presumably been maintained by the Whitbread family until then.

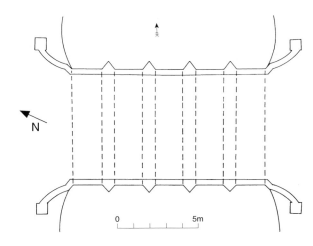

Fig 25 Cardington bridge: ground plan

STRUCTURAL EVIDENCE

The bridge appears to be almost unaltered from Smeaton's original design except that it is in brick rather than stone. As such it is the earliest surviving brick bridge known in the county.[6]

It is a simple structure, 21 ft 6 in (6.6m) wide between parapets. Of the five segmental arches, the three central ones are each 5 ft 10 in (1.8m) wide, with the end arches only slightly narrower at about 5 ft 6 in (1.7m). Unlike the hump-backed appearance of earlier small bridges there is only a slight rise over the arches. The main elevations are mostly in yellow gault brick, with the arch soffits in red brick. Limestone was used for the cutwater caps, keystones, and copings.

The arches are separated by very narrow tall piers, which are protected by slight plinths round the base at water level. Keeled half-pyramid cutwaters, capped by limestone copings, rise to the arch springing on both faces of the bridge. The arch rings, which spring from the cutwater capstones, are formed by alternating a brick stretcher with two headers (though this design has not always been respected in later repairs). There are projecting limestone keystones at the crown of each arch. Those over the three central arches on the west face read, from north to south:

J Smeaton	S W	J Green
ENG	1778	SURV

referring to the designer, the sponsor and the surveyor in charge of works.

The spandrel walls are plain, rising to a double course of projecting bricks which forms a string course beneath the original brick parapet. The shape of the parapet follows Smeaton's design except that the terminals, capped by low stone pyramids, are square instead of rounded. Two brick panels have also been added on both faces over the cutwaters flanking the central arch. These are an original feature as the limestone copings reflect the panelling.

Of Smeaton's original design only the invert has been lost. His drawing shows it to have been framed in timber, surrounding the whole bridge. No traces can now be seen as it has been replaced in concrete. At some time, the original stone kerbing along the road side has been replaced in modern materials, and small-scale repairs to the elevations have been carried out using bricks of various colours, giving the bridge a more mottled appearance than it first had.

NOTES

1   Beds RO: W 712
2   Beds RO: W 2/2; a transcript is published in J Wood, *Cardington & Eastcotts*, Bedfordshire Parish Surveys 3, 1985, Map 2
3   Ruddock, 1979, 83; H Dickinson & A Gomme (eds), 'A Catalogue of the Civil and Engineering Designs 1741-1792 of John Smeaton preserved in the Library of the Royal Society', *Newcomen Society Extra Publication* 5, 1950, 100
4   Beds RO: QBM 1, 103
5   Beds RO: QBP 9
6   TL 083 493; HER 5633

SUSPENSION BRIDGE, Bedford

Jefferys' county map of 1765 shows a bridge crossing the northern arm of the River Ouse east of Bedford town centre, on what is now the site of the Suspension bridge. It is likely that this served for agricultural purposes only, providing access to cart hay from Longholme island.

The present bridge was built by John J Webster in 1888 as part of the Embankment landscaping scheme. Bedford

Fig 26 Suspension bridge, Bedford, from the east

Corporation had purchased Mill Meadows on the south of the river in 1883[1] and a bridge was needed to link the embankment on the north side with the newly acquired meadows. At first a low flat girder bridge was proposed but this would have obstructed river traffic. After a competition to design a bridge, judged by Webster himself, he proposed the elegant bow string lattice girder design that was subsequently built. It is 6 ft (1.8m) wide with a 100 ft (30.5m) span. It is only 15 ft (4.6m) above water level at its centre. It has a concrete deck laid on iron plates (manufactured by Westwood and Bailey) between the girders. The ironwork was made in Bedford by E Page and Co for £304, with stone abutments supplied by the Corporation.[2]

The bridge is the first example of a suspension bridge to be erected in the county.[3]

NOTES
1 R Wildman, 'The Suspension bridge, Bedford', *Bedfordshire on Sunday,* 15.4.1979
2 'Bedford in 1888', *Bedfordshire Times and Independent,* 1888
3 TL 057 495; HER 4519

BEDFORD BRIDGE

No traces remain of Bedford's medieval bridge, known in the old Borough records as the 'Great Bridge'. It was demolished in 1811 and replaced by the present bridge on the same site.[1]

THE SAXON CROSSING

Typical of the many '-ford' placenames, Bedford had been an important river crossing long before the bridge was built. The town developed from a Saxon *burh* which was established beside the ford sometime between the 8th and the 10th century.[2] The Anglo-Saxon Chronicle records that King Edward the Elder occupied the town and established a southern *burh* across the river in 915 to provide a defence against Danish raids.[3] The first bridge may have been built at this time, to link the two halves of the town.

If there was a bridge in Saxon times, it would almost certainly have been of wooden trestle construction. There is no evidence that timbers found west of the present bridge in 1974[4] were either Saxon, or even the remains of a bridge.

MEDIEVAL HISTORY

The Great Bridge became an important factor in the growth of medieval Bedford. Apart from fords at Great Barford and Tempsford, there were no river crossing points on public highways downstream of Bedford until St Neots some thirteen miles away. The bridge therefore had a marked influence on the prosperity of the town, attracting traffic both from long distance routes and from local travellers.

Specific references to Bedford bridge first appear in the late 12th century, when Simon de Beauchamp (who held the barony of Bedford) granted a bridge chapel to St John's Hospital.[5] Tradition has it that the first stone (as opposed to timber) bridge was built using rubble taken from Bedford castle after its destruction in 1224,[6] although the official records of the time specifically granted stone from the castle to St Paul's Church, and to Cauldwell and Newnham Priories.[7]

A new bridge chapel (or 'oratory') was built by townsmen some time before 1331, and endowed with property; a chaplain, John de Budenho, was appointed to take services and to use the income to keep the bridge in repair.[8] In 1332 a rival cleric, John de Derby, was appointed by King Edward III, and the sheriff was ordered to install him, but he was forcibly prevented from taking possession by the mayor and assembled townsmen.[9] The dispute dragged on, to the detriment of the chapel and the bridge, and in 1344 the king ordered an inquiry into the facts of the case.[10] It appears that the inquiry eventually found in the king's favour in the matter of appointing the chaplain, but the townsmen's role in maintaining the bridge was recognised in 1349, by the granting of pontage to 'the mayor, bailiffs and goodmen' of Bedford.[11]

Further grants of pontage were made in 1359 and 1383.[12] The collection of tolls seems to have had an effect on the trade and movement of goods within the town, possibly involving separate markets on each side of the river. For example, in the 12th to 14th centuries pottery vessels from Lyveden in Northamptonshire were more common on the north side of the river, while Oxfordshire products predominated in the south.[13]

Evidently the chapel had fallen out of use by the mid-15th century, as in 1452 the will of Thomas Chalton, Alderman of the City of London, left 40s towards the 'making of the new chapel of St Thomas'.[14] Further wills of 1502 and 1503, including one from London, left money for its repair.[15] This new chapel only functioned as such for a short time, as there was no record of it in the Chantry Certificates compiled in Edward VI's reign in the mid-16th century.[16] Bequests to the repair of the bridge itself continued throughout the 16th century.[17]

By 1569 two annually elected bridgewardens were appointed to look after the bridge and to administer the tolls.[18] They also collected 6d fines from prisoners held in the northern gatehouse (formerly the chapel), which functioned as a gaol after 1589.[19] The southern gatehouse later held the magazine and store for the county militia.[20] By the 17th century the Chamberlain (the Borough treasurer) was held responsible for maintenance.[21]

Steps to improve the river crossing were first taken in 1765. The Borough council removed the gatehouses and repaired and capped the parapet wall with Portland stone. Six lamps were placed on the bridge.[22] The gatehouses, especially the northern one, had hindered coach traffic as it entered the town, but even with this improvement the bridge was still an obstacle to traffic. There were also frequent problems with flooding: in 1792 'the Ouse rose within 3 ft of the top of the middle arch of the Bridge'.[23]

The bridge was described in 1803 as 'very ancient, narrow, inconvenient, and dangerous ... and the Piers of the said Bridge are so constructed as to impede the Current of the said River in Time of Flood to the great Injury of the Inhabitants of the Town'.[24]

THE MEDIEVAL BRIDGE FROM ILLUSTRATIONS

Some idea of the character of the old bridge may be obtained from a series of 18th century drawings of its downstream elevation,[25] though no views of the upstream face survive (see Figs 27 and 28). The bridge had seven arches, though often only five were visible in the drawings; they were usually shown as rounded but occasionally as pointed. They had ribbed soffits, suggesting a 13th century or later date for their construction. The piers are usually shown with square-ended buttresses on the downstream side. These are more emphasised in later views, which show them tapering towards the parapet,

Fig 27 Old Bedford bridge, before 1765 (Beds Record Office: Z 48/50)

Fig 28 Old Bedford bridge, after demolition of the gatehouses (Beds Record Office: BP 28/4)

although in one case the buttresses are absent altogether. One view from the north shows a triangular refuge on the upstream side, suggesting that there were pointed cutwaters of typical medieval design on that face.[26]

Many of the illustrations show both gatehouses. The chapel is easily identifiable as the north gatehouse, despite later alterations. The stone-built portion, carried out to the east of the bridge on a low ribbed arch, occupied a typical bridge chapel location. The remainder of the north gatehouse was probably later, spanning the carriageway between the chapel and the cutwater opposite. The southern gatehouse was also of stone, with a timber storey above which looks like a later addition.

The dimensions of the Great Bridge are known from a description by Dr Broade, physician to Henry VIII, in 1526. It was 330 ft (100m) long and 13½ ft (4.1m) wide, with a parapet 3½ ft (1m) high.[27]

PROPOSALS FOR A NEW BRIDGE

The 18th and 19th century were a period of major architectural development in many cities and towns. As part of this trend, from the mid-18th century onwards, architects were often employed to design and build bridges incorporating the latest architectural fashions. At first only the large cities could afford new bridges (Westminster bridge, London, 1735; Essex bridge, Dublin, 1753-5; Blackfriars bridge, London, 1760-9), but by the late 18th century

many of the dilapidated narrow medieval bridges of the smaller county towns were also being replaced (typical examples of these new bridges, in the classical style, were erected at Shrewsbury, 1769-74, Worcester, 1770-81, and Henley, 1781-4).[28] The situation at Bedford was typical of this trend of urban improvement.

Bedford's medieval bridge, with its decaying rubble walls and protruding gatehouse foundations, was a prime candidate for replacement. The restrictions which the bridge caused for both traffic and water flow were useful arguments in favour of change, although a further motivation among the advocates for a new bridge may have been the more visual effects of urban improvement and the public benevolence which it would demonstrate.

An Act of Parliament 'for the Improvement of the Town of Bedford, and for rebuilding the Bridge over the River Ouze, in the said Town' was passed in 1803.[29] There was little further progress until 1809 when the Bedford Improvements Commission advertised for plans and estimates.[30] John Wing (whose father, also called John Wing, had built Girtford bridge) was one of the Improvement Commissioners, and he supplied an estimate of £12,850 for a bridge 26 ft (7.9m) wide.[31] A revised estimate of £14,950, allowing for a width of 30 ft (9.2m), was accepted in 1810.[32] (After this date, John Wing no longer attended Commissioners meetings until his contract for the bridge had been completed.)

A provision of the 1803 Act permitted the collection of

tolls to repay monies raised through public subscription, and a further Act in 1810[33] allowed additional funds to be raised. Amongst the chief contributors to the project were the Duke of Bedford and Samuel Whitbread.[34]

DEMOLITION AND REBUILDING

In 1811, a temporary timber crossing was built to the east of the medieval bridge, and demolition began. Contemporary reports and public notices give a fascinating insight into the structure and condition of the old bridge, and show that even at the time questions were raised as to the necessity of its replacement.

The first signs of dissent are recorded in a broadsheet issued in 1811, '... it having been inferred by some Persons, because Parts of the Bridge are got to Pieces with great difficulty, that the whole Structure was sound, and that there was no necessity for a new Bridge ...'[35]

A report by John Wing to the Bedford Improvement Commissioners, dated 3 November 1809, was reproduced:

'... I find that many parts of [the old bridge] are in dilapidated and ruinous state, more particularly the Foundations and the Springing of the Arches, as well as the Walls on each side, and leaving out of the question the irregular appearance and the enormous thickness of the Piers, one of which is 20 ft [6.1m] and another 22 ft [6.7m] in thickness, and the whole occupying one-third of the width of the River, and appearing to be built only of Rubble ...'

George Cloake wrote to the Commissioners on 29 June 1811:

'I have examined the remains of the old Bridge, consisting of 3 Arches and 4 Piers ... it has been composed only of loose Rubble, cemented by a grout composition of Stone, Lime and Sand. Very little hard Stone has been used with the same to unite or cement Bond and strengthen the Structure. There appears to have been a sort of Rib formed in the Arches, of Welldon Stone, and the Rubble filled in between, and a great body of Rubbish filled in over the Arches, so that time has made it a sort of solid Mass; but it is a Mass of that sort, which, though very difficult to get asunder, is ill calculated to carry or resist any weight or pressure; and the Arches, at the Springings, appear to be in a very bad state, more particularly those that were taking down which came under my inspection; they were all decayed at their Springings, and had they not have been taking down would have fallen down. The piers appear to be composed of the same rough Materials as the Arches, with very little square or solid Stone, ill calculated to bear great weight, and, in my opinion, by no means proper or safe to carry any new weight (which the new Bridge will of course require) ...

'The Foundations of all the Piers which have hitherto been taken down were built upon Piles, about 3 ft [0.9m] long, driven through a stratum of Clay, lying on a Rock of solid Stone. Mr Wing is digging out the Foundations, so that the Piers may stand on the Rock itself.'

Similar descriptions could equally well apply to any of the great medieval bridges across the Ouse (Turvey, Harrold, Bromham). They were all constructed of thin masonry walls built from unsquared local stone, retaining an infill of earth and rubble. The use of piles, driven through the river bed to support and spread the weight of the stone structure, was a tried and tested medieval technique. The Commissioners clearly felt the need to produce evidence to support their decision to demolish the medieval bridge; but there remains the possibility that, given proper maintenance, it could have survived to the present day.

The construction of the new bridge involved the use of coffer dams around the pier bases, to allow excavation down to bedrock. The new piers were thus built on a solid foundation. Work progressed through 1812: in May, 'Mr Wing was fortunate enough last week to raise the remaining Pier and Abutment Pier above the Water Line and today he is placing centres for the 3 Arches and raising all the piers above the Water Line'.[36]

The new bridge was completed in 1813, at a cost of £15,137, and opened on 1st November. Tolls were charged until 1835, after which free passage was permitted.

WING'S BRIDGE

Wing's bridge is 305 ft (93m) long, and its original width was 30 ft (9.2m). It has a very pronounced hump-backed appearance due to the progressively increasing arch span from the outer arches to the centre arch. There are five elliptical arches: the outermost, arches 1 and 5, have spans of 32 ft 6 in (9.9m); arches 2 and 4 are 37 ft 3 in (11.4m); and the centre arch, arch 3, is 43 ft 6 in (13.3m). Although other bridges of the period were being designed with much more level road surfaces, the hump was necessary at Bedford. The river banks on either side were very low; this made a shallow gradient impractical, as there had to be clearance for both flood water and river craft. The gradient was more pronounced on the south bank, so in March 1813 the Improvements Committee instructed that the road there should be raised to make a more gradual approach to the bridge.[37]

Wing's bridge is of simple design. The stonework is smooth-faced, regularly coursed ashlar in both spandrel walls and arch soffits, and the voussoirs plain with deep V-joints between them. There is a single keystone at the crown of each arch. There are rounded cutwaters on both faces of the bridge, each capped by a low dome immediately above the arch springing; this treatment was typical of the advances and changes in bridge design by this period.

Above the string course, two more recessed courses support a balustraded parapet. The balustrade consists of stretches of closely spaced balusters interrupted over the piers and arch crowns by rectangular fascias or panelling. These are 5 ft (1.5m) long over the arch crowns, doubling in size over the piers to 10 ft (3m). Each is decorated by a

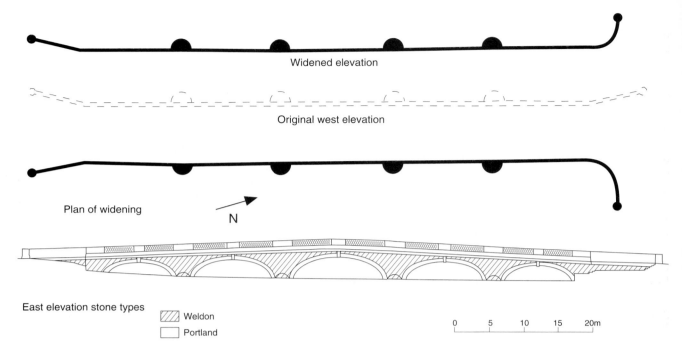

Widened elevation

Original west elevation

Plan of widening

N

East elevation stone types

Weldon

Portland

0   5   10   15   20m

Fig 29 Wing's bridge, Bedford: plan, elevation and stone types

Fig 30 Wing's bridge, Bedford: from the south-east (Beds Photographic Services)

rectangular 'medallion' except over the central arch. Here there is a raised winged rectangular panel over the keystone of the east face carrying an inscription commemorating the opening of the bridge:

'This bridge was designed and executed by John Wing, of Bedford. It was begun on the twenty-sixth day of April, 1811, completed and opened for public use on the first day of November, 1813.'

A similar panel on the west face was plain. The balustrading does not continue beyond the river bank, but the parapets over the wing walls are solid; each finishes in a large octagonal terminal.

The spandrel walls up to the string course are of Weldon stone from Northamptonshire. A much harder wearing limestone from Portland in Dorset was used for the string course, balustrade, fascias and voussoir stones (Henman's reference[38] to the use of Bramley Fall stone from Yorkshire for the architectural detail and Portland facing for the spandrels and soffits, is incorrect). 'Scotch' granite was used to cobble the road surface, which was 18 ft (5.5m) wide; there were two broad pavements, each 6 ft (1.8m) wide, also paved with Scotch granite, though Yorkshire kerb was originally proposed.[39]

A toll house was situated at the north-west corner of the bridge, and was apparently a very ornate octagonal structure. After tolls were abolished in 1835, the building was converted into a Post Office.

20th CENTURY WIDENING

By the end of the 19th century, the pressure of traffic on the bridge was so great that a second river crossing was erected at 'Cauldwell bridge' (Prebend Street) in 1884. By 1913, the volume of traffic had again increased, and plans to widen Wing's bridge were drawn up.[40] These were eventually implemented in 1938-40, when the bridge was widened in concrete along its western side to 54 ft (16.5m). The former toll-house was demolished to accommodate the line of the widened road.

Considerable effort was taken to harmonise the new work with the old. The original west face was carefully dismantled and the stone saved. It was then re-assembled to mask the new concrete construction and cannot now be distinguished from the original facade except for the concrete arch soffits.

In the early 1980s repairs to the stonework of the bridge were carried out, using Portland stone for the architectural details and Clipsham stone for the spandrel walls.

NOTES

1 TL 050 495; HER 1020; see also Peter McKeague, 'Bedford Bridge, old and new', *Beds Mag* 22 no 172, Spring 1990, 165-168; Bedfordshire County Planning Department, *'Discovering our Past' Broadsheet Series* no 14, 'Bedford Town Bridge', Martin Cook, 1991; *Lockgate* I no 2, Jan 1962, 19-23; no 3, Apr 1962, 41-44

2 See D Hill, 'Late Saxon Bedford', in D Baker *et al*, 'Excavations in Bedford', *Beds Archaeol J* 5, 1970, 96-98, and J Haslam, 'The Origin and plan of Bedford', *Beds Archaeology* 16, 1983, 29-36, for alternative views of the date of the first Saxon *burh*

3 Hill, *op cit*

4 *Beds Archaeol J* 9, 1974, 78

5 *BHRS* 9, 1925, 177, 180

6 W N Henman, 'Bedford bridge and its story', *Bedfordshire Times*, 31 Oct 1913

7 Close Rolls: *Rot Lit Claus* i, 1204-1224 (1833), 632a

8 *Cal Patent Rolls*, 1330-4, 148; *Rolls Parl* ii, 100

9 *Cal Patent Rolls*, 1330-4, 304, 351

10 *ibid*, 1343-5, 404

11 *ibid*, 1348-50, 254; other summaries of the dispute can be found in J J Jusserand, *English Wayfaring Life in the Middle Ages*, 1961 ed, 30; *VCH Beds* 3, 1912, 30; Henman, *op cit*; Jervoise, 1932, 90-91; D & S Lysons, *Magna Britannia,* vol I pt I, Bedfordshire, 1813, 49; Godber, 1969, 117-118)

12 *Cal Patent Rolls*, 1358-61, 252; 1381-5, 238

13 E Baker & J Hassall, 'The Pottery', in D Baker *et al, op cit,* 180

14 *BHRS* 14, 1931, 126

15 *BHRS* 45, 1966, 32 no 69, 37-38 no 80; *BHRS* 37, 1957, 13 no 37d

16 J E Brown, *Chantry Certificates for Bedfordshire,* nd

17 Beds RO: eg ABP/R 2 no 95, f90v – Thomas Knight of Bedford, 13s 4d, 1522; ABP/R 3 no 124, f59v – Richard Wayneman of Bedford, 3s 4d, 1526

18 Godber, 1969, 194

19 *BHRS* 36, 1956, 20n. There is no evidence that John Bunyan was ever imprisoned in the Borough gaol on the bridge. He was held in the County gaol (on the corner of Silver Street and High Street) for several years

20 Henman, *op cit*

21 *BHRS* 26, 1949, 108

22 Lysons & Lysons, *op cit*, 49; Henman, *op cit*

23 Beds RO: BC 536, T O Marsh papers

24 43 George III, c128; Henman, *op cit*

25 Beds RO holds an extensive collection of illustrations of the old bridge (see illustrations catalogue for details)

26 Beds RO, Z 48/49; reproduced in *Beds Mag* 22 no 172, Spring 1990, 165

27 Quoted by Henman, *op cit*

28 Ruddock, 1979

29 43 George III, c128 (copy in Beds RO: Z 417/56)

30 Beds RO: Micf 15, Bedford Improvements Commission Minutes, 7.7.1809

31 *ibid*, 3.11.1809

32 *ibid*, 7.8.1810

33 50 George III, c82 (copy in Beds RO: Z 417/56-7)

34 Henman, *op cit*

35 Beds RO: W 1/81

36 Beds RO: W 1/84, letter from Theed Pearse, 10.5.1812

37 Beds RO: Micf 15, *op cit*, 2.3.1813

38 Henman, *op cit*

39 Beds RO: Micf 15, *op cit*, 4.5.1813

40 Henman, *op cit*

CAULDWELL BRIDGE
Prebend Street, Bedford

The iron bridge in Prebend Street, which survived until 1992, was a relatively late example of its type, having

Fig 31 Cauldwell bridge, Prebend Street, Bedford, before demolition in 1992

been constructed in 1883 to relieve the traffic on Wing's bridge in the town centre to the east.[1] It also served the rapidly expanding areas in Bedford between and around the railway stations. Although long multiple span iron river bridges had been constructed over rivers like the Thames from the early 19th century there were no earlier examples in Bedfordshire.

John J Webster was the bridge's architect; although he was also responsible for the Suspension bridge on Bedford's embankment in 1888, he was more famous for constructing piers, such as Bangor and Dover.[2]

The bridge was opened in 1884.[3] It comprised three cast iron arches with brick and stone piers and abutments. The ironwork was produced by Goddard and Massey of Nottingham, and the masonry by Pilling and Co, Manchester.[4] The braced girders were cast in one piece. Decorative trefoil cutouts filled the spandrels above and the trefoil theme was reproduced over the entire length of the parapet railing. Much of this ironwork above the structural girders was cast in short sections, presumably for ease of transportation.

The piers were faced in yellow brick below the arch springing but with stone above. There were low cutwaters up to springing level on each face of the bridge; these too were in brick with low domed stone capstones. The piers carried up to parapet level as slightly projecting square-ended buttresses interrupting the iron railings. Between springing and road level they were faced with rusticated stone but there were plainer limestone blocks above. The surviving abutments are similarly faced with stone and to the south there is a long brick-faced raised approach.

The brick abutments and piers eventually proved unable to take the weight of the iron structure and the traffic it was carrying, and Prebend Street bridge was replaced by the new County bridge in 1992.

NOTES
1   TL 046 493; HER 4527
2   *ibid*
3   Beds C C, *Industrial Archaeology of Bedfordshire,* 1967, 14
4   The architect and builder were commemorated by plaques on the bridge

KEMPSTON HARDWICK BRIDGE

Lying on an ancient lane forming the historic parish boundary with Wootton, Hardwick bridge[1] is first mentioned in c.1430 in the court rolls of Kempston Brucebury manor.[2] It is recorded again in 1516/17 when Bartholomew Jordan remembered the bridge in his will, leaving 3s 4d to 'Hardwyke bridge'.[3] Apparently the Parson or Pierson family were liable for its upkeep, as in 1625 Thomas Parson was presented in the manor court because he had not made 'a sufficient foot causeway beyond the bridge called Hardwick bridge in the way there leading aforesaid to Hardwicke and that he has not made the aforesaid bridge sufficient'.[4] Ten years later William Pierson was presented for taking away stepping stones at the bridge in the King's highway.[5] Little is known of the bridge's later history.

The bridge surviving today has an unusual appearance. There are two tall rounded arches, almost horseshoe-shaped, separated by a relatively narrow central pier. There is a keeled cutwater with an irregular plinth on the upstream face. The cutwater rises to the arch springing, where it is capped by a steeply inclined half-pyramid coping. The downstream face is plain. The limestone stonework is of noticeably more substantial proportions than that seen on the Ouse bridges of both medieval and 18th/19th century date. Above the arches, the low brick parapets are obvious additions, particularly that on the downstream side which rests on the arch ring. The wing walls either side of each parapet have been extended and built up round the brickwork.

Much repair work was carried out in 1986, including the insertion of concrete reinforcing arches beneath the arch soffits. Cracking in the arch soffit has been thought to indicate that the bridge was widened to about three

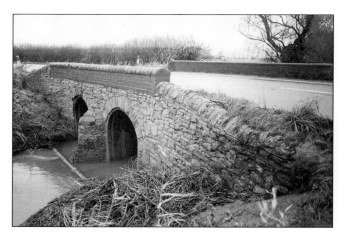

Fig 32 Kempston Hardwick bridge from the south-east

times its original width,[6] but the absence of any break in the coursing suggests that the cracking was no more than a structural weakness and that the bridge is of one period, with minor additions. The cutwater style is typically 18th or 19th century, confirming that the present bridge post-dates the earlier documentary references. The rough quality of its execution, and the plain downstream face argue for a local imitation of styles developing more widely in the 18th century. Despite the lack of documentation, the bridge is an interesting, relatively unaltered, example of its kind, a late bridge adopting ideas current in 18th and 19th century designed bridges but lacking full understanding of how those structures worked.

NOTES

1 TL 024 451; HER 4442
2 Beds RO: PE 466/7/1
3 *BHRS* 37, 1957, 254
4 Beds RO: PE 466/2 m8
5 Beds RO: PE 466/2 m15
6 Wood J, *Kempston,* Bedfordshire Parish Surveys 2, 1984, 10

BROMHAM BRIDGE

The present bridge of twenty-six arches carried the A428 west from Bedford towards Newport Pagnell and Northampton until the opening of Bromham bypass in 1986.[1] Twenty arches span the broad floodplain to the east whilst the remaining six arches carry the road over the river and Bromham mill races. An extensive repair programme was undertaken by the County Surveyor for the Department of Transport between 1985 and 1988.

EARLY HISTORY

Bromham bridge, which was known as Biddenham bridge until the 17th century, was first mentioned in the Pipe Rolls for 1224 when 4s was spent on repairs, suggesting that there had already been a bridge here for some time.[2] This early reference is unusual: the Pipe Rolls were records of Crown revenue collected by the county sheriff, and it may be that the repairs were carried out by the sheriff using royal money.

In contrast to other bridging points along the River Ouse, there is no evidence of an important earlier crossing here. An ancient ridgeway which runs from the south-west along the Kempston and Stagsden parish boundary appears to have crossed the Ouse further north at Clapham ford. An east-west route may have passed through Biddenham, crossing the river west of the village and south of the bridge. It was only with the establishment of the bridge that the present main road west from Bedford appears to have been laid out, cutting through the open field pattern of the northern part of Biddenham parish (Fig 33).   In 1281, the bridge was the cause of a tragic death, when 'a serious frost so injured Biddenham bridge that it gave way and a woman was carried away by the stream. She sat on an ice floe as far as Bedford bridge, when she was seen no more.'[3]

A chantry chapel, dedicated to Saints Mary and Katherine, was founded by Matthew of Dunstable in 1295 'for the safety of travellers who were in danger from thieves'; there was a priest to say prayers for the founders, and to collect and spend alms to maintain the bridge and to help travellers.[4] The chapel benefited from a substantial gift of houses and land by Simon de Wolston in 1325.[5]

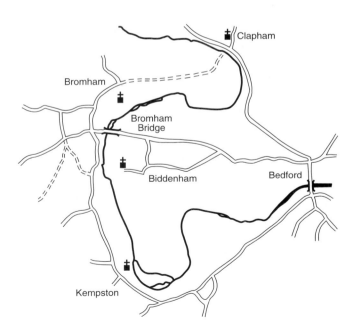

Possible road layout before construction of Bromham bridge

Possible road changes after construction of Bromham bridge

Fig 33 Bromham bridge: early road system

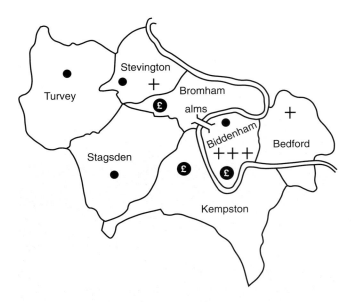

● parish charged with repair of bridge, 1383

+ late medieval bequest

£ rents of land held by bridge chapel

Fig 34 Bromham bridge: sources of medieval income

Surrounding parishes also contributed towards the bridge's upkeep. In 1383 the townships (ie parishes) of Stagsden, Stevington, Turvey and Biddenham were each charged by the Crown with failing to repair it, although the township of Turvey disputed this charge three years later.[6]

In the late 15th and early 16th centuries, Bromham benefited from several bequests, principally from parishioners in Biddenham,[7] but even from as far away as London.[8] Bequests such as these highlight the significance of the bridge as a through route for long distance traffic.

The various sources of income for the bridge in the late medieval and early Tudor period are summarised in Figure 34. As far as can be seen the parishes were liable only for the causeway, but not for the river arches which would have been maintained through the income of the chapel.

Chantry chapels were suppressed in the reign of Edward VI as a consequence of the Reformation, and of the end of the practice in the reformed Church of England

of saying masses for the souls of the dead. Before its closure in 1553, the chapel at Bromham bridge held land in Biddenham and Kempston, and 'the quarry pyttes in Bromham'.[9] Stone from the quarries had probably been used in repairs.

In c.1630, a survey of bridges in Willey Hundred set down the liabilities for repair as follows:

'Biddenham Bridge: one double high Arch repaired by the Inhabitants of the Parish of Biddenham the other twenty Arches of the long Bridge repaired by the County. Bromham Bridge: three high Arches repaired by the County'[10]

The Biddenham 'double high arch' was the present arch 23, and was probably so named because this was where the foot causeway (the 'long bridge') and the access ramp for road vehicles met, forming two arches side by side.

The County ordered that repairs be carried out in 1651,[11] and further work is commemorated in an inscription of 1685 which still survives on the north face of arch 25.

One further 17th century reference gives some insight into the strategic importance of bridges in times of war. In 1646 during the Civil War, Henry Lowens, a Royalist, guarded the bridge with a chain and posts against Parliamentary soldiers.[12]

THE MEDIEVAL BRIDGE

Little remains of the medieval bridge in the present structure. Only the original four river arches (arches 23-26) are visible opposite the mill (Fig 36). Each is a rounded arch with dressed limestone soffits, supporting a carriageway of about 11 ft (3.4m) wide. Further traces of the old bridge were found during drainage improvements to the deck of the bridge in 1988, when medieval cutwaters were revealed on the north side of piers 22/23 and 25/26, behind 19th century re-facing work.

Two illustrations of the long horse and foot bridge survive, a drawing by Thomas Fisher of 1812 (Fig 37)[13] and a plan drawn up in preparation for its replacement the following year (see Fig 35).[14] The latter shows it to have been about 6 ft (1.8m) wide, with rounded arches separated by piers which had pointed cutwaters on the upstream face. The piers were irregularly shaped and spaced, perhaps reflecting piecemeal development.

The chantry chapel stood at the west end of the bridge,

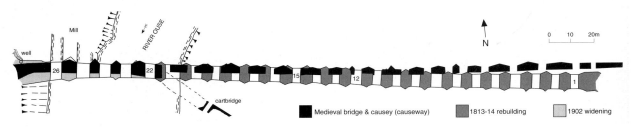

Fig 35 Bromham bridge: phase plan

Fig 36 Bromham bridge: north face of river bridge

on the north side of the road. Until the late 19th century remains were still visible in the south end of the miller's house at Bromham Mill: part of a pointed window 8 to 9 ft (2.4-2.7m) wide could be seen in the south wall, along with other architectural fragments.[15] This part of the miller's house was demolished in the early 20th century.[16]

17th TO 19th CENTURY

There was a long sequence of mostly small-scale repairs by the County throughout the late 17th and 18th centuries, but even in the late 18th century all vehicles still had to cross the flood plain by a cart track and climb on to the bridge at the river bank. In response to this, the Quarter Sessions sought an estimate in 1769 for 'making the Horse Bridge [ie the causeway] fit and capable for carriages to pass and repass thereon'.[17] A sum not exceeding £100 was authorised in 1792[18] and a description of 1793 noted 'five collateral arches added for safer passage of carriages over deepest parts of meadow at high water'.[19] The work seems to have involved the improve-

Fig 37 Bromham bridge: drawing by Thomas Fisher, 1812

Fig 38 Bromham bridge: remains of cart bridge

ment of the existing cart track by raising it on to a cause-way and inserting flood arches at its western end; vehicles could then join the foot causeway and main bridge at pier 21/22. The south face of this pier, before it was widened in 1902, splayed southwards to accommodate the cart bridge joining it at an angle.

The cart track and bridge is shown on estate maps for both Biddenham (1794) and Bromham (1798);[20] the Bromham estate map shows cutwaters along its entire length. Traces still survive: part of one pier, a paved and cobbled invert, and the very fragmentary remains of a second pier are exposed in the side of a stream in the meadow south of the bridge (Fig 38). Further east, part of a hollow way leading to the cart bridge can be seen immediately south of the modern road.

The existence of both foot and vehicle causeways, running side by side, is confirmed in contemporary notes made by Rev Thomas Orlebar Marsh: 'Bromham – 2 bridges; one by the side of the other; both very long'. He recorded floods in September 1797, when 'the water came all over Bromham long bridge (the rd [road] long bridge)', indicating that the deck of the cart ('road') bridge was at a lower level than the foot causeway.[21]

SALMON'S BRIDGE OF 1813-14

The problem of vehicular access across the flood plain was finally solved in 1813 with a scheme by Robert Salmon to demolish the horse and foot bridge and replace it with flood arches carrying a 16 ft 6 in (5.0m) roadway.[22] This work was completed by 1814, and survives today almost in its original form (Fig 39).

Salmon's bridge, although very much in the tradition and character of medieval bridges, displays remarkably uniform characteristics. The cutwaters are triangular, with slightly concave faces, rising to form refuges along both sides of the carriageway. The apex of each cutwater is pinched giving the parapets a smooth curved appearance. Although most of the arches are rounded or semi-circular with a consistent span of 12 ft 6 in (3.80m), every fourth arch from the east end is more elliptical, spanning 15 ft 5 in (4.70m). Only at arch 21, the last of Salmon's arches, is there any variation. The arch is elliptical, with a vastly increased span of 21 ft 4 in (6.50m). This may reflect an awkward join between the old bridge and the new work.

The floor of each arch was protected by a pitched lime-stone invert, dry set in a yellow clayey sand (Figs 40 and

Fig 39 Bromham bridge: south face of 1813-14 flood arches

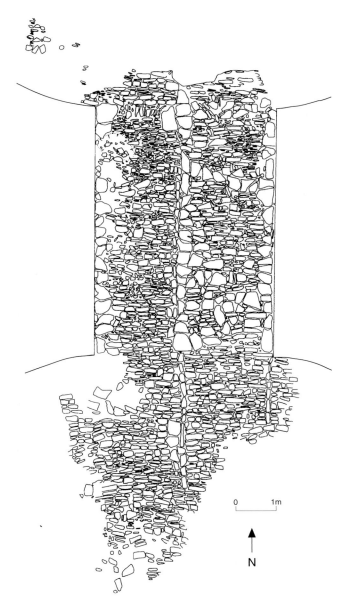

Fig 40 Bromham bridge: plan of invert, arch 20

Fig 41 Bromham bridge: limestone invert

41). The style of these varies from arch to arch, probably a result of later repairs; in some the stones are aligned parallel to the carriageway, in others at right angles; in some arches there was a mixture of the two. The upstream cutwaters of piers 19/20 and 20/21 were also surrounded by pitched stones. Downstream the inverts extended for up to 8 ft (2.5m) beyond the arch, to protect against scour. When first laid the inverts must have protected a wide area around the bridge. The extent of later repair and patching provides ample evidence to the destructive power of the river when swollen by flood water.

The river bridge, although still only 11 ft (3.4m) wide, was not widened or rebuilt at this time, either because it was considered adequate for the traffic of the period or perhaps because the Quarter Sessions had been alarmed by the spiralling costs of Wing's bridge in Bedford which had only recently been completed. It was however resurfaced, and traces of this were exposed during repair work in 1988. Several areas of pitched stone were revealed, set in a similar yellow clayey sand to the inverts below the bridge.

Repairs were needed to the new bridge within a few years. One of the arches was damaged by severe floods in 1823,[23] and small-scale repairs were carried out almost every year. By 1850 it was in a considerable state of dilapidation;[24] after carrying out repairs, the County Surveyor summed up the problem:

'What I have done has been executed substantially and with the best quality Materials which I regret to state was not originally the case for a worse constructed Bridge and with worse Materials could not have been built.'[25]

The Quarter Sessions bridge minutes in 1855 record a delay to repairs 'because they have not until quite lately begun to quarry the harder kind of stone in the Bromham pits which we have been waiting for'.[26]

Salmon's rebuilding, hampered by a low budget, may not have been so selective, using poorer quality materials from the upper levels of nearby quarries.

20th CENTURY

In 1902, increasing traffic pressure on the bridge, with its narrow bottleneck at the west end, resulted in the County Council widening the remaining arches over the river to match the width of the flood arches (Fig 42). Straight joints in the soffits of the four westernmost river arches (23-26) show where the widening abuts the early bridge. Part of arch 22 may also have been widened at this time, but the apparent straight joint in part of arch 21 soffit is illusory, resulting from structural weakness. The most distinctive features of this phase are the two refuges corbelled out over the downstream (south) face of the bridge on piers 23/24 and 25/26; the former incorporates a date plaque commemorating the widening.

At the north-west end of the bridge, the wing wall was realigned and carried over a niche, traditionally the 'Holy Well' associated with the nearby chapel. Whatever the

Fig 42 Bromham bridge: south face of river bridge, showing 1902 widening

antiquity of the well the flight of steps and the niche were constructed during the 1902 works.

Resurfacing work in 1988 uncovered traces of the bridge's more recent history during the Second World War, echoing its earlier defence in the Civil War. At the Biddenham end there were six rows of brick-lined sockets set in concrete (Fig 43), suitable for anchoring a blockade.[27]

NOTES

1   TL 011 506; HER 998; see also Peter McKeague, 'Bromham Bridge', *Beds Mag* 21 no 165, Summer 1988, 205-208; Bedfordshire County Planning Department, *'Discovering our Past' Broadsheet Series* no 9, 'Bromham Bridge, Peter McKeague, 1988; *Lockgate* II no 14, Jan 1969, 218-222; P Tritton, 'Fit and Capable for Carriages to pass and repass thereon: Bromham Bridge', *Beds Mag* 20 no 153, Summer 1985, 34-38
2   Jervoise, 1932, 84
3   *VCH Beds* 3, 1912, 44
4   *VCH Beds* 3, 1912, 49; J E Brown, *Chantry certificates for Bedfordshire*, nd, 14
5   Beds RO: TW 103; *VCH Beds* 3, 1912, 49. Although generally accepted (eg by Brown, *op cit*) that Simon de Wolston refounded the chapel, the document specifically refers to a grant to an existing chapel
6   Selden Society, *Public Works in Medieval Law* 32, 1915, 1
7   eg *BHRS* 58, 1979, 31, no 26 (1493); *BHRS* 45, 1966, 21-2 no 47 (1501); 88-89 no 177 (1507); 90-91 no 180 (1508); 50-51 no 108 (1509)
8   *BHRS* 58, 1979, 142-144 no 112 (1528)
9   Beds RO: CRT 130 BRO 7, Summary history of Bromham Bridge, by Record Office staff; Brown, *op cit,* 13-15
10 Beds RO: P 27/1/5
11 Beds RO: TW 841
12 Beds RO: VHV 1 (VCH manuscript notes for Bromham parish)
13 John Fisher, *Collections Historical Genealogical and Topographical of Bedfordshire,* no 18 p61
14 Beds RO: PB 7/2
15 William Marsh Harvey, *The History and Antiquities of the Hundred of Willey in the County of Bedford,* 1872-8, 51; *Beds Times* 3.2.1899, p3
16 It is shown on the 1901 edition of the OS 1:2500 map, but not on the 1926 edition
17 Beds RO: QBM 1, 18 (1769)
18 Beds RO: QBM 1, 28
19 Beds RO: VHV 1
20 Beds RO: X 1/51, Biddenham Estate map, 1794; X 152, Bromham estate map, 1798
21 Beds RO: BC 536
22 Beds RO: QSR 21, 1813, 218; QBM 1, 66-70
23 Beds RO: QBM 1, 141 (1824)
24 Beds RO: QBC 1, County Surveyor's report, Easter 1850
25 Beds RO: QBC 1, County Surveyor's report, Michaelmas 1851
26 Beds RO: QBC 2, 1855
27 For an illustration showing how such a road-block would work, see Council for British Archaeology, *20th Century Defences in Britain,* 1995, 89

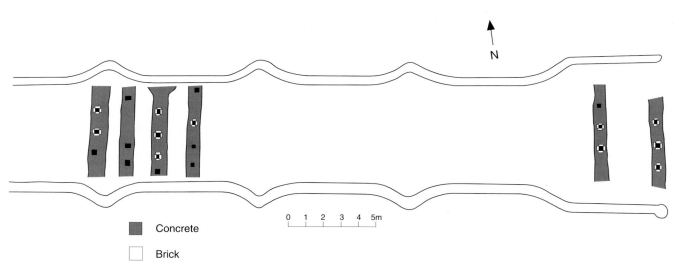

Fig 43 Bromham bridge: plan of World War II vehicle barrier at east end

TYMSILL BRIDGE, Bromham

The road from Bromham to Stagsden is carried over the Serpentine Brook on the parish boundary, just to the west of Bromham village, by what appears from the road to be a comparatively modern bridge. Underneath there are traces of a medieval limestone arch which has been widened several times.[1] It can be identified from Bryant's map of 1826 as Tymsill bridge,[2] but has also been known as Thistley Green bridge from the late 19th century.

HISTORY

Tymsill bridge is mentioned in three 16th century wills. In 1507 Goditha Wodyll left 2 measures of barley towards its repair[3] and Robert Sampsoun left 20d in 1515.[4] In 1593, Stephen Coxe remembered four bridges in the parish, Hellingreene, Beerye Meede, Wick End and Timsell bridges.[5] During the mid-18th century and after 1814 the bridge was managed by the Bedford to Newport Pagnell Turnpike Trust. In 1817 the Quarter Sessions approved a grant of money to the Trustees for repairing a bridge over the Stagsden brook, perhaps referring to Tymsill or to Wick End bridge nearby.[6] It became a county bridge after the winding up of the Turnpike Trust in 1870.

Fig 44 Tymsill bridge: soffit from the north, showing successive widenings

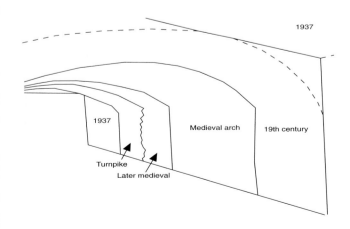

STRUCTURAL EVIDENCE

The single span has been widened on four occasions with straight joints visible in the soffit between the different periods. The earliest work, in rubble limestone, is only 7 ft 6 in wide (2.3m), the same width as Sutton packhorse bridge. Vehicles could probably have crossed if there was no parapet. As traffic increased, the bridge was widened twice in limestone on the upstream (south) side, first to 11 ft (3.4m) and then to about 15 ft (4.6m). It was later widened again, with limestone abutments and a brick arch, on the downstream side, increasing the width to over 19 ft (5.8m). Finally in 1937 the bridge was extended in concrete on both elevations, and the present stone parapets added; it is now over 32 ft (10m) wide.

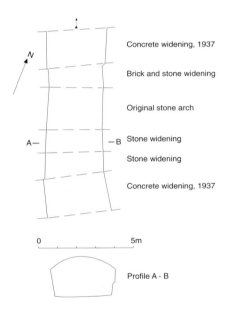

Fig 45 Tymsill bridge: ground plan and profile

It is difficult to date such a small structure, especially as its early history is poorly documented. The short segmental arch of the original span is typical of late medieval bridges, perhaps suggesting a 15th century date. This is not inconsistent with the earliest references in wills. Apart from the 1937 extensions, none of the widenings is recorded, but it is tempting to associate them with the ever-increasing volume of traffic. Perhaps after an initial widening in the 17th or 18th century the bridge was further widened by the Turnpike Trustees (possibly in 1817), then by the county in the late 19th century (in limestone and brick) and again in concrete in 1937.

NOTES

1   SP 999 503; HER 3203; see also Peter McKeague, 'Two little-known Bedfordshire Bridges', *Beds Mag* 21 no 167, Winter 1988, 281-284

46

2 Bryant marks it 'Timsit Bridge'
3 *BHRS* 45, 1966, 88-89 no 177
4 *BHRS* 45, 1966, 91 no 181
5 Beds RO: ABP/W 1593/64
6 Beds RO: QBM 1, 99 (1817)

OAKLEY BRIDGE

HISTORY

Where the road between Oakley and Bromham crosses the River Ouse, there was not a substantial road bridge until the early 19th century. Before then, the river flowed in four separate channels, on the northernmost of which lay Oakley mill (Fig 46).[1] Small foot bridges may have crossed each of the watercourses, but vehicles used a ford slightly downstream of the mill. A stone arch associated with the mill still survives at the north end of the present bridge.

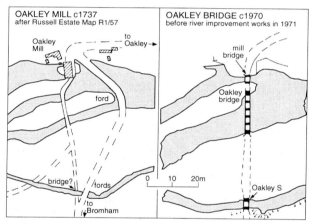

Fig 46 Oakley bridge: location plan, comparing the earlier mill and fords with the 19th century crossings

In the early 19th century the Duke of Bedford, who held the mill as lord of the manor of Oakley Reynes, evidently decided to demolish it and to build a new stone bridge. In 1813, the estate accounts record 46 yards (42m) of stone work and 37 yards (34m) of stone pitching, as well as 'digging and cleaning away for arches and filling up between walls ...'.[2] Further accounts can be found in the estate records for 1815, with additional works continuing to 1818.[3] The Rev Thomas Orlebar Marsh recorded: '31 July 1815. Saw Oakley new bridge of 5 arches and with a parapet wall this bridge is nearly finished and is passable'.[4]

STRUCTURAL EVIDENCE

At the north end of the bridge, the old mill arch survives, and is separated from the main river bridge by a small island (Fig 47). It has been widened on both faces in order to line up with the new 1815 bridge; its original profile was rounded, but the widenings are elliptical, giving it an irregular appearance.

The main river bridge is unusually narrow for an early 19th century structure. It is 12 ft 6 in (3.80m) in overall width and 10 ft 2 in (3.10m) between the parapets, permitting only one way traffic. It is also of very simple design, having five rounded arches with no cutwaters.[5] There are two unusual oval 'buttresses' on the outside face of the east parapet between the river and mill bridges. They serve no structural function and may be part of the former mill buildings. A free-standing circular pillar of limestone to the north has been capped with a marker to indicate the exceptional height of a flood on 1st November 1823.

LATER REPAIRS

When the Oakley estate was sold in 1918, the auctioneer's catalogue stated that Oakley House and the lands in hand were to be sold as a lot with the liability to repair the chancel of the church, maintain the bridge over the back

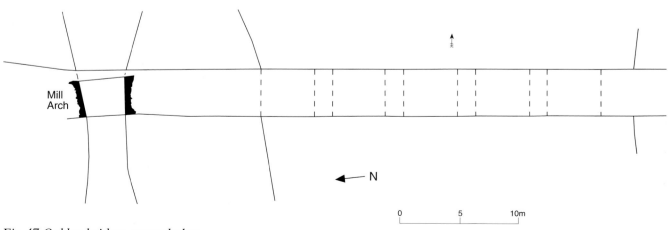

Fig 47 Oakley bridge: ground plan

Fig 48 Oakley bridge: river bridge and mill arch from the north-east

brook (the detached arch on the Bromham side) and a third of Stafford bridge;[6] the main river bridge was not mentioned among the manorial responsibilities. Liability was disputed between the County Council and the Duke of Bedford, but it was successfully proven that the bridge had been extensively repaired by the Duke's estate in 1911.[7] '1911' may still be seen carved onto the downstream face of the second arch from the south. In spite of this, the County Council resolved that Oakley bridge was a County bridge in 1919.[8]

Buttresses have been added to the downstream (east) face of the bridge sometime this century, and improvement works in 1971 considerably altered the nature of the river. In 1982 the upstream face of the bridge was rebuilt above the arches in Portland limestone.

OAKLEY SOUTH BRIDGE

Oakley South bridge (Fig 49) lies over a side channel of the river, connected to the main bridge by a low causeway crossing an island.[9] The single rounded limestone arch has projecting keystones on both faces. It may also have been constructed in 1815.

This bridge has the distinction of being the only historic road bridge in the county which still retains timber railings, though the present ones are replacements dating from a repair scheme of 1987.

NOTES
1   Beds RO: R 1/57 Estate Map 1737
2   Beds RO: R box 643, no 97
3   Beds RO: R 5/1326, R 5/1353
4   Beds RO: BC 532

Fig 49 Oakley South bridge
(Beds Photographic Services)

5   TL 008 529; HER 1722; see also Peter McKeague, 'Radwell, Felmersham and Oakley Bridges', *Beds Mag* 22 no 171, Winter 1989, 100-103
6   Beds RO: AD 1147/18
7   Beds RO: Hi C P 21, 7a, Aug 1919
8   Beds RO: Hi C M 6, 162, Feb 1919
9   TL 008 528; HER 15728

STAFFORD BRIDGE

The medieval Stafford bridge[1] connected the parishes of Oakley and Pavenham on what was once a main highway leading from Bedford to the river crossing at Harrold.

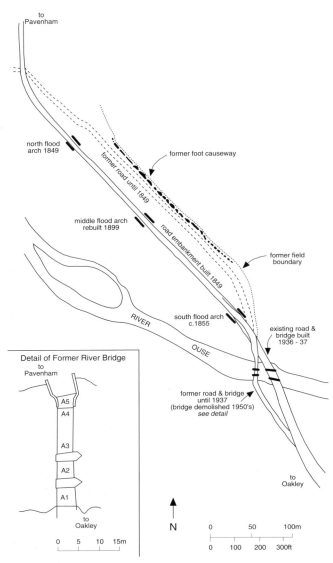

Fig 50 Stafford bridge: plan

Although now demolished, the structural development of the bridge can be reconstructed from descriptions, plans and illustrations. It consisted of a road bridge of four arches over the river, with a long foot causeway of thirty or more arches over the low meadows in Pavenham. There were no flood arches on the Oakley bank, which rises steeply from the river. In this account, the river arches are numbered from the Oakley (south) side.

The present bridge was built in 1936-37 about 40 feet upstream.

EARLY HISTORY

The place name 'Stafford' first appears in 1227 when 'Richard De Pabeham fell from a certain mare into the water of Stafford so that he died'.[2] As Richard appears to have been crossing by a ford, this may suggest that the bridge had not yet been built.

The first references to a bridge are in wills dating from the 16th century. The earliest are from 1505, when John Stowghton of Oakley left '2 strikes of barley', and John Skott of Oakley 3s 4d.[3] In 1522, Thomas Knight of Bedford left 10s 'for repairing the long causeway beyond Stafford bridge'.[4] The bridge was evidently widely used, as people from Podington, Stevington, Felmersham, Pavenham, Oakley and Bedford made bequests for its repair.[5]

The c.1630 survey of bridges in Willey Hundred records that the two high arches on the Pavenham (north) side were maintained by Lord Vaux in respect of his lands in Pavenham (Cheneys manor) and by the Lord of 'Steventon' (who held Bury Farm, Pavenham). The two Oakley arches, in Stodden Hundred, were maintained by the Lord of Oakley and by the inhabitants of the parish. The 'thirty and [blank in document] little arches' in Pavenham (the foot causeway) were repaired by the County.[6]

THE MEDIEVAL BRIDGE

The river bridge

Something of the character of the medieval bridge can be reconstructed from later records. The piers had triangular

Fig 51 Stafford bridge: drawing by Thomas Fisher, 1815 (Beds Record Office: X 376/40)

cutwaters upstream and slight rectangular buttresses downstream. An 1815 illustration by Thomas Fisher[7] suggests that arches 3 and 4 were pointed, in contrast to the rounded arches on the Oakley side (Fig 51). It is an interesting variation in style which probably reflects the different manorial responsibilities.

A sketch elevation of 1853 records the river bridge as 79 ft and 6 in (24.2m) long.[8] Of the four stone river arches only the two next to the Oakley bank (arches 1 and 2) survived into the twentieth century.[9] Both were ribbed rounded arches. Originally each had three chamfered ribs, but only the east and central ribs survived. At arch 1 the western rib had been replaced by a double ordered arch ring with narrow chamfers on the arrises. The soffit was partly rebuilt, set lower than the original work and abutted up against the dressed vertical face of the central rib. The western rib of arch 2 had been replaced by a single ordered arch ring slightly overhanging the soffit, but lacking the broad chamfer of the ribbing.

The causeway

As late as 1755 some of the causeway arches near the Pavenham end were still wooden, as instructions were issued to rebuild them in stone.[10] In 1819 the causeway was recorded as 416 yards (380m) long but only 5 ft (1.5m) wide, with thirty-one arches.[11] Part of its plan survives, showing twenty-eight arches.[12] The arches nearest the river are missing (the drawing has been cut), but their line can be fixed by a later field boundary (Fig 50). The causeway had triangular cutwaters on the upstream face for most of its length, stopping before the edge of the flood plain. On the downstream side there are three paths shown leading up onto the causeway at intervals; these may indicate piecemeal extension.

LATER HISTORY

In the late 18th century, the County kept the foot causeway in repair by payment of an annual salary of £4 to a Mr Harrison.[13] The river bridge appears to have been less well maintained: in 1759 the Quarter Sessions expressed concern to Sir Thomas Alston, Joseph Franklyn of Bury Farm, the Duke of Bedford and the parishioners of Oakley about the condition of their respective arches.[14]

By 1819, the County Surveyor reported that, while the arches and foundation appeared quite sound, the superstructure of the river bridge was so dilapidated and narrow that it was extremely dangerous for passengers, 'it being but 8 ft 6 in [2.6m] wide in one place and without sidewalls [parapets]'. He proposed that the bridge be widened by 2 ft (0.6m) to 10 ft 6 in (3.2m), by stretching wooden beams across the cutwaters on the upstream (east) side; and that a guard rail should also be added on that side, and a 9 inch (230mm) thick brick wall on the west side.[15] This was carried out at the expense of the Duke of Bedford and Mrs Winstanley of Pavenham, who were jointly found liable for repairs.[16] The stepped triangular cappings of the cutwaters visible in later photographs date from during or after the alterations, as they were built up against the horizontal timber beams of the widening.

During the mid-19th century, there was occasional discussion about improving the Pavenham approach to the bridge.[17] The road was often flooded and vehicles

Fig 52 Stafford bridge: before demolition, from the east (Co Engineer)

could not negotiate the narrow foot causeway. Eventually in 1849, the old causeway was demolished. An extra flood arch (arch 5) was added to the north end of the river bridge and a new road embankment built across the flood plain. This had a single land arch towards the north end.[18]

In 1853, one of the Pavenham river arches (arch 4) was washed away by floods.[19] Mr Tucker of Bury Farm, Pavenham, who was now responsible for arches 3 and 4, alleged that this was because the new embankment reduced the potential waterway by 490 sq ft (45.5 sq m), and therefore flood water could not escape properly. To solve the problem, construction of a new bridge was considered,[20] the cost to be split equally between the private owners (the Duke of Bedford and Mr Tucker) and the county. This plan fell through, and arch 4 was repaired by Mr Tucker 'under protest'.[21] Probably soon after this the limestone arch at the south end of the embankment was added to relieve flood pressure.[22] A third arch in the centre of the causeway was rebuilt with iron girders in 1899.[23]

By 1905 the Pavenham arches of the river bridge (arches 3 and 4) had been replaced by girders stretched from pier 2/3 across to arch 5.[24]

The bridge remained in private hands until 1923 when the County Council resolved to assume responsibility.[25] Soon after this the bridge was widened again, from 10 ft 6 in (3.2m) to 14 ft (4.25m).

THE MODERN BRIDGE

By 1936 the bridge was unsuitable for traffic, and the present bridge was built alongside. It has three skew arches and appears to be a typical limestone bridge, but in fact the stonework is only a cladding of local and Weldon stone built over a core of reinforced concrete. The Pavenham embankment was extended to the new bridge, and its alignment improved by widening the south flood arch on the west side.[26] On the Oakley side a new embankment was constructed to join the new bridge with the old road.

The old bridge was partly dismantled, originally leaving the two medieval arches standing. These were still visible in the 1950s but few traces now remain.

NOTES

1 TL 009 544; HER 207; see also Peter McKeague & Martin Cook, 'Stafford Bridge', *Beds Mag* 22 no 174, Autumn 1990, 228-230 and Bedfordshire County Planning Department, *'Discovering our Past' Broadsheet Series* no 13, 'Stafford Bridge', Martin Cook, 1990
2 *BHRS* 3, 1916, 171-2
3 *BHRS* 37, 1957, 29 no 76, 30 no 78. A 'strike' was a measure of dry corn, in some places the equivalent of a bushel (*Oxford English Dictionary* vol X, 1933, 1125); its precise Bedfordshire meaning is unknown
4 Beds RO: ABP/R 2 no 95 f90v
5 *BHRS* 37, 1957, 203; Beds RO: ABP/R3 no 62 f28r
6 Beds RO: P 27/1/5 Turvey
7 Beds RO: X 376/40; published in John Fisher, *Colls Hist Gen & Topog Beds*, no 74, p173

8 Beds RO: PB 4/2, 1853
9 Evidence from photographs taken by the Co Surveyor, 1936/37
10 Beds RO: QBM 1, 14; QSR 9, 1755, 65
11 Beds RO: QBM 1, 116
12 Beds RO: PB 6/1
13 Beds RO: payment recorded in QSR 13, 1777, 147; 15, 1786, 147; 16, 1788, 157
14 Beds RO: QBM 1, 16
15 Beds RO: QBM 1, 114-115
16 Beds RO: QBM 1, 121-122
17 Beds RO: eg QBM 1, 265 (1835), 268 (1836), 330 (1848), 333 (1849)
18 Beds RO: QBM 1, 336; PB 4/1
19 Beds RO: QBM 1, 357-360; PB 4/2
20 Beds RO: QBM 1, 363 (1853)
21 Beds RO: QBM 1, 367 (1853)
22 Beds RO: QBM 1, 381-383
23 Beds Co Surv Drawing Br/C15/193/2
24 Ian Pitts, 'Stafford Bridge', *Beds Mag* 19 no 152, Spring 1985, 315-317
25 Beds RO: CRT 130 PAV 4, Notes by Record Office staff
26 Co Engineer plan: BR/C15/195-1, Jan 1935

RADWELL BRIDGE

Radwell bridge[1] was built by Thomas Morris in 1766 for £292 10s;[2] it replaced a ford, and significantly upgraded the road to Milton Ernest and thus to the Bedford-Rushden turnpike which was created in 1727.[3] No original documentation survives, but it was probably financed by the parish or, less likely, through public subscription.

It was originally of five arches (those at the south end of the present bridge), rounded in shape and constructed of limestone rubble. They are separated by large piers which have keeled cutwaters with stepped half-pyramid caps on the upstream face. This feature, with the cutwaters capped at the level of the arch springing, copies the new styles of piers being introduced into British bridge building from the turn of the 18th century, but the piers are in every other way of typical medieval style. They are still massively constructed, with no attempt to reduce the size of piers in proportion to the arch span in order to lighten the structure. The roadway is 12 ft 6 in (3.8m) wide. Rev Thomas Orlebar Marsh recorded that lime used for the bridge was made at Pavenham.[4]

The bridge was not at first maintained by the County and in 1775, when the Quarter Sessions found half the bridge already to be 'ruinous and in great decay', an indictment against the County for repairs was dismissed.[5] However in 1805, the Assizes ordered the County to repair the bridge,[6] and in 1806 an arch was added on the Radwell side.[7] Pier 5/6, which is at the position of the original north abutment, is noticeably narrower than the other river piers, showing where this sixth arch was added.

The Rev Thomas Orlebar Marsh recorded the effects of several floods in the early 19th century. In 1821, a man named Allen rowed his boat over the top the bridge.[8] In

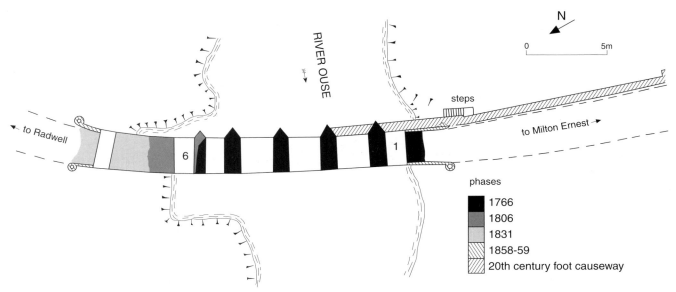

Fig 53 Radwell bridge: phase plan

October 1923, the oak copings were washed away.[9] The floods of February 1831 caused more damage, and extensive rebuilding costing £139 6s 0d was carried out.[10] The small flood arch at the north end was possibly added at this time.

More work was done in 1858-59 when the wing walls were rebuilt with massive rounded terminals, and repairs to the cutwaters carried out.[11]

In modern times, a footbridge across the broad floodplain has been carried over the first two arches at the south-east corner by a concrete beam; access to the roadway is given by a break in the bridge parapet. This continues the long tradition of narrow foot causeways on the Bedfordshire floodplain of the Ouse.

NOTES

1 TL 005 572; HER 5671; see also Peter McKeague, 'Radwell, Felmersham and Oakley Bridges', *Beds Mag* 22 no 171, Winter 1989, 100-103

2 William Marsh Harvey, *The History and Antiquities of the Hundred of Willey in the County of Bedford*, 1872-8, 286

3 *BHRS Survey of Ancient Buildings* 3, 1936, 13

4 Beds RO: BC 536

Fig 54 Drawing of Radwell Hall and bridge by Thomas Fisher, 1816 (Beds Record Office: Z 60/32)

Fig 55 Radwell bridge: east face

5   Beds RO: QSR 13, 1775, 142
6   Beds RO: QBM 1, 45 (1805)
7   Beds RO: T O Marsh, Natural History Diaries, vol I, 261;
    Harvey, *op cit*
8   Beds RO: BC 534
9   Beds RO: BC 536
10 *BHRS* 40, 1960, 142-143; Beds RO: QBM 1, 240-1, 251 (1832)
11 Beds RO: QBM 1, 395, 397 (1858), 404 (1859); QBC 2

FELMERSHAM BRIDGE

This five-arched bridge lies mostly within Sharnbrook parish.[1] However, it is more closely associated with Felmersham, having been financed and built through the determination of Felmersham parishioners. Stonework repairs and resurfacing were undertaken by the County Engineer in 1993.

HISTORY

Despite being almost enclosed by a broad loop in the river Ouse, Felmersham had no medieval road bridge. The settlement was isolated, with no main highway passing through the parish. There is some evidence for bridges and fords from the 17th century: there was a wooden bridge ('Coney bridge') at Pinch Mills, and a ford on the ancient road from Sharnbrook to Felmersham; further east there was a footbridge and ford at Stoke Mills, and the ford at Radwell which is recorded in 1708.[2] The first road bridge in the parish was built at the Radwell ford in 1766. At Felmersham itself, the ford by the church continued in use into the 19th century.

The first indication that the inhabitants of Felmersham wanted a bridge came at the enclosure of Sharnbrook in 1809. They petitioned the Enclosure Commissioners to consider setting out a public carriage road or bridleway over Sharnbrook meadow to the ford below Felmersham church as the existing road was in a very bad place and unsafe for both carriages and 'passengers on horseback'. They made clear their wishes to build and maintain a bridge on the new road.[3] After nine years' delay, presumably to raise funds, work on Felmersham bridge began in 1818.

The construction work is relatively well documented for a bridge built by a parish rather than by the County. The progress of works was recorded in the diary of Edward Arpin, the parish clerk of Felmersham.[4] Work started on 20th May 1818, the first arch was turned on 13th June and the second fourteen days later. The third arch was turned on 3rd August, the fourth on 22nd August, and the fifth and last on 8th October. On 14th November 1818 the bridge was finished.

Records made by Rev Thomas Orlebar Marsh offer additional (and partly contradictory) information.[5] According to Marsh, the bridge was built by local masons, John and Samuel Bell of Radwell, using stone quarried in the parish[6] and sand from near the ford.[7] By 31st August 1818 (the Monday of the Felmersham Feast), when he said the bridge was first passable for pedestrians and horsemen, 'a collection was made for the workmen, and they dined together on the Bridge, and were moreover entertained with music by the Rusticks of the Place'.[8] He also records that the bridge, which cost £600, was not finished until December 8th 1818.[9]

Despite the speed with which the bridge was built, and although the line of the new road on the Sharnbrook side

Fig 56 Felmersham bridge: drawing by Thomas Fisher after flood damage, 1819 (Cecil Higgins Art Gallery)

had been laid out, there was a dispute about who should make and maintain the road, with the onus apparently falling on Felmersham. The outcome of the dispute is not known, but by January 1820 the road had been completed. Meanwhile there were problems with the bridge. On Sunday, 24th February 1819 a flood brought down 'much of the gravelly substance of the bridge and defaced and much injured 2 of the arches on the Felmersham side and on the Thursday morning early 6 yards more of the wall on the same side'.[10] The scene was captured by Fisher in his drawing of the bridge (Fig 56),[11] which shows that about a 50 ft (15m) length of the bridge collapsed on the west or upstream side, at the Felmersham end. Arpin records that on the 14th October 1819 the second arch that had collapsed was turned. After a year and nineteen weeks the repairs had been completed. Marsh added that the bridge had been strengthened and repaired and provided with a raised wooden footway at the Sharnbrook end.[12]

There were further severe floods on Christmas Day 1821, bringing down the walls of the bridge again, in October 1823 when the parapet was carried away,[13] and again on Midsummer Day 1827.

The bridge was evidently privately maintained until about 1875 when maintenance accounts are first found in Quarter Sessions records.[14] Further repairs were needed in 1881 both to the river bridge[15] and to the timber footbridge,[16] and again to the river bridge in 1919.[17]

STRUCTURAL EVIDENCE

The bridge is almost entirely constructed in rubble limestone. There are five rounded arches (numbered 1 to 5 from the Felmersham bank) of almost uniform span, their dimensions of 16 ft 9 in (5.10m) being close to the original contract specifications.[18] The bridge is 18 ft (5.5m) wide supporting a 14 ft 6 in (4.45m) wide carriageway between the stone parapets. These end in large square terminals which are capped with similarly shaped copings. The parapets themselves are capped with triangular blocks of dressed Weldon stone.

There are keeled cutwaters on the upstream elevation, with the stepped half-pyramid cappings typical of the local bridge-building style of the period. They are of similarly

Fig 57 Felmersham bridge: from the south-west (Beds Photographic Services)

massive proportions to the Radwell cutwaters, reminiscent of the traditional medieval building style rather than a familiarity with more modern engineering techniques. At Felmersham, however, they were not part of the original design. They are not shown on Fisher's 1819 illustration, and during repair works in 1993 it became clear that they had been largely butted up against the west elevation, with only the slightest attempt at tying them in to the existing stonework. It is probable that they were added to the bridge during the repairs after the flood of 1819.

The arch floors are protected by a series of extremely well-preserved pitched stone inverts. That nearest Felmersham (arch 1) is usually dry and is easily accessible from the bank (Fig 59). It is composed of tightly set pitched limestone blocks laid parallel to the carriageway, similar to some of the inverts at Bromham. Unlike Bromham, however, the Felmersham inverts are 'framed and set' within horizontal timber sill beams laid against the arch faces. A series of vertical piles helps to hold the beams in position. The inverts, forming a continuous 'pavement', extend downstream of the bridge for 4 ft 3 in (1.30m) and traces of a similar upstream apron survive at pier 1/2. Originally this extended right up to the apex of the cut-

Fig 59 Felmersham bridge: invert, arch 1

water but is now in a rather fragmentary condition. The stonework in both invert extensions is noticeably larger, with the upstream side being paved rather than pitched.

The repairs of 1919 by the County Surveyor's department are commemorated in a datestone on the downstream face of pier 3/4. This work involved refacing much of the downstream (east) elevation from the central arch to the north end of the bridge, and rebuilding and raising the parapets. The new work is clearly visible in the arch rings, where the voussoirs are much more regular in shape than elsewhere on the bridge. The repairs are an early example of the use of strong cement. When new voussoirs were inserted, neat liquid cement was poured into the joints; this resulted in serious cracking in the arch rings, because the joints became too rigid to adjust to subsequent settlement stresses.

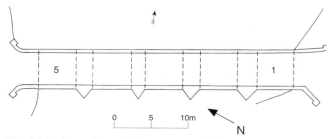

Fig 58 Felmersham bridge: ground plan

To the north of the bridge a concrete 'plank' foot causeway resting on solid concrete piers extends over the Sharnbrook floodplain north of the bridge. It is a 20th century replacement of the earlier wooden structure.

NOTES

1 990 578; HER 1058; see also Peter McKeague, 'Radwell, Felmersham and Oakley Bridges', *Beds Mag* 22 no 171, Winter 1989, 100-103; *Lockgate* II no 5, Oct 1966, 78-80
2 Beds RO: ABE 2, 1708 (Glebe terrier), transcribed in CRT 170/2/15/2
3 Beds RO: GA 2569, 20.11.1809
4 *BHRS* 40, 1960, 137
5 Beds RO: BC 529-534
6 Beds RO: BC 531; W E Draycott, *Grain and Chaff: thrashing out the history of Felmersham, Bedfordshire,* 1986, 22
7 Beds RO: BC 529, 534
8 Beds RO: BC 534
9 Beds RO: BC 531, 532
10 *BHRS* 40, 1960, 138; Beds RO: Thomas Orlebar Marsh, Natural History Notebooks I, 261
11 Beds RO: Micf 66, FB 204 no 534 (from an original drawing in the Cecil Higgins Art Gallery, Bedford)
12 Draycott, *op cit,* 24
13 Beds RO: BC 536
14 Beds RO: QBC 5
15 Beds RO: *Beds Mercury* 4.6.1881
16 Beds RO: *Beds Mercury* 23.7.1881
17 Beds Co Engineer' drawings: BR/U29/331-2
18 Beds RO: CRT 130 FEL 12 – Photocopy of articles of agreement, 21 May 1818, between John & Samuel Bell, masons, and Joseph Swannell & Joseph Paine of Felmersham, farmers

HARROLD BRIDGE

The ancient bridge crossing the River Ouse at Harrold has three distinct parts. Six arches, 213 ft (65m) in length, carry the road over the river; these form the Great or River bridge. On the south bank of the river there is a short causeway of 49 ft (15m), then a further nine flood arches cross the low flood plain for about 197 ft (60m). South of the road bridge, a foot causeway, or 'causey', of a further twenty arches, runs for about 650 ft (200m) parallel to the present road.[1] Major structural repairs to the bridge and causeway were carried out by the County Council between 1986 and 1992.

Various individuals and bodies were responsible for the maintenance of different parts of the bridge throughout its history. This has led to the development of a complex structure of many periods and in a variety of styles.

For ease of reference, the arch numbers used here are those now in use by the County Engineer. Different numbers used in documentary sources are shown in inverted commas.

EARLY HISTORY

The earliest crossing at Harrold was a ford which connected an ancient (possibly even prehistoric) route from Pavenham and the old village of Chellington to another which ran northwards towards Irchester in Northamptonshire. The Roman town at Irchester was preceded by a late Iron Age settlement, and the routeway to it shows every sign of being at least as old, with its close relationship to the natural terrain and the evidence of extreme wear in places. Where it crosses the river at Harrold, the line of the access to the ford from the north bank is still preserved in the broad verge east of the modern road.

A bridge is first mentioned in documents dating from 1136-46, which refer to 'three acres of my lord's meadow next to the place of Harewold bridge'.[2] Its construction (of which the date is unknown) improved communications between Bedford and Northampton, and had a significant effect on the road system and nearby settlements. The ancient road through Chellington was superseded by that which now runs southwards from the bridge, between the historic parishes of Carlton and Chellington. The increased traffic, and the income which this generated, seems to have been influential in the migration of the scattered settlements of Carlton and Chellington to the roadside. Both parish churches now stand isolated.

There are further passing references to the bridge in the Coroner's Rolls of 1274 ('in Carlton field ... a footpath which extends towards Harrold bridge'),[3] and in the Hundred Rolls of 1279.[4]

The importance of the bridge in late medieval times is reflected in the number of bequests made towards its repair. For example, Thomas Russell of Stevington left two bushels of barley in 1509[5] and Richard Rabett of Podington 'half a quarter of barley' in 1511.[6] In 1516, Thomas Amowr (sic) of Carlton bequeathed 12d,[7] and John Russell of Stevington two bushels of barley in 1529.[8]

A causeway at Harrold is specifically mentioned in the will of John Heywood of Podington in 1516/17.[9] Then in 1539, Reginald Hall of Harrold left the following instruction:

'I (will that my) executors shall cause to make a stone arche in the causey (between Carlton) and Harrolde' and if his children should die 'I will that my executors shall make another arch of the bridge.'[10]

Early documents from Harrold give the first indication that the lord of the manor had some responsibilities for repairs. The manorial bailiff's accounts for 1532[11] record:

'Payd for reparacyons done apon the kyngs bryge at Harrold

Item to our carpenter for fallyng of tymber and hewing the same for the sayd bryge	12d
Item to the sawyers for sawing the same tymber the wyche was 200 fote and a half at 13d every 100	2s 8½d
Item for careying the same tymber to the sawe pitt	6d

Item to the carpenter and his man for leying
the planks apon the bryge and mending the
same for two dayes and a half at every
day 11d   2s 3¹/₂d

                                              sum   6s 6d'

This itemised repair consisted of breaching the gap
between two bridge piers by laying down timbers,
presumably after the collapse of a stone arch. Later
evidence shows that this was arch 14.

In about 1630 responsibilities for maintenance were
defined in detail as follows:-

'four high Arches the first Sir Richard Chetwood the
second the Earl of Kent the third and fourth the Lord
Mordaunt. The One and Thirty arches of the Long Bridge
the County repairs.'[12]

The individuals mentioned were lords of the adjacent
manors of Odell, Harrold, Carlton and Chellington, and
they were responsible for the first four arches from the
Harrold bank. The thirty-one County arches can be
accounted for in the modern bridge by the two southernmost river arches, the nine flood arches, and the twenty
arches of the foot causeway. As provision for a County
rate to finance bridge repairs was only established in
1530/31, someone else must have maintained these arches
before that date. There was a tradition in the last century
that the foot causeway was once known as 'the Nuns'
bridge', having been built by a former Prioress of Harrold
Priory.[13] Although the foot causeway crosses the end of
the 'Nuns' Meadow' in Carlton, there is nothing to
confirm this tradition. On the other hand, Harrold Priory
did have lands in Turvey parish to which access through
Carlton was required, and as a major land owner it may
have been liable for many of the arches. This is supported
by the fact that the County eventually took over responsibility for it: this was usually the case when bridges fell
into disrepair which had been maintained by religious
houses until the Dissolution in the 16th century.

The earliest surviving reference to maintenance by the
County is in 1651, when the Quarter Sessions ordered
repairs to be carried out under the supervision of Roger
Pitkyn and Thomas Billing.[14]

THE MEDIEVAL BRIDGE

The early foot causeway

The present foot causeway consists of twenty arches, but
inspection of the soffits of the flood arches shows that it
originally extended right up to the river crossing. The
stonework of the old causeway can still be seen beneath
flood arches 1, 2, 3, 5 and 6, behind later widenings; its
downstream (east) elevation is still exposed at arches
5 and 6, and the beginnings of a medieval triangular
cutwater are visible on the west side of the pier at the
same point.

Differences in style throughout the causeway suggest
three main periods of development. Most of the work,
except the southernmost five arches (at the Carlton end),
is typically medieval, built of massive piers with
triangular cutwaters on the upstream (west) elevation (Fig
60). The width varies between 7 ft 9 in (2.4m) and 8 ft 10
in (2.7m). However, the arches concealed in the later road
bridge have round profiles whereas the remainder are
pointed. This change may be significant, reflecting
development from the round arches used in early
medieval times to the gothic style (with pointed arches)
which became popular in the late 12th or early 13th
century. The earliest phase of the flood arches may
therefore be the oldest surviving part of the bridge.

Fig 60 Harrold bridge: the causeway from the north-west

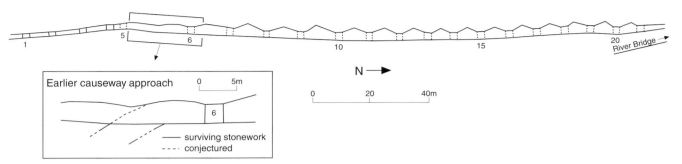

Fig 61 Harrold bridge: plan of causeway

The south (Carlton) end of the causeway shows a marked change of character. There are no cutwaters, and the pathway narrows from 8 ft 6 in (2.6m) to only 6 ft (1.8m). Evidence recovered during repair work in 1992 confirmed that these arches were a later extension. Between arches 5 and 6, traces were found of an earlier approach ramp, retained by stone walls, which rose from the present road on to the causeway at what is now arch 6 (Figs 61 and 62).[15] It is tempting to associate one or two of the new arches with Reginald Hall's will of 1539 (see above). Certainly the causeway had reached its present length by c.1630.

The relationship between the early foot causeway and the river bridge abutment is obscured by the earthen mound which separates them. This mound originated as an earthen ramp which gave access for vehicles on to the original river bridge at its south-east corner. The eastern face of this ramp was defined by a low retaining wing wall continuous with the east elevation of arch 10, the southernmost river arch. The lower courses of stonework on this face are inclined and can be traced rising over arch 10 and up to the spandrel wall of arch 11, showing the line

of the ramp (Fig 63). The steepness of the climb on to the river bridge at this early period may explain why the ford to the east of the bridge continued in use.

The modern passing bay is constructed upon the remains of the earthen mound. Its west side was probably originally defined by a continuous wall from the foot causeway to the west elevation of arch 10.

The widening of the flood arches

At an unknown date, the nine causeway arches nearest the river were widened to take vehicular traffic across the lowest part of the flood plain (Fig 64). In order to accommodate the new vehicle approach ramp the eastern face of the causeway was kicked back from about 50 ft (15m) north of causeway arch 20 (the original face was revealed when the modern road surface was removed during the 1990 repairs). Flood arches 1 and 2 were widened on the east side, and all the flood arches except arch 1 were widened to the west by inserting an additional limestone arch ring which sprang from the cutwaters (Fig 65). (Evidence of this widening does not occur in arches 4, 7, 8 and 9 as they have since been rebuilt.)

Fig 62 Harrold bridge: footing of early causeway approach ramp, between arches 5 and 6

Fig 63 Harrold bridge: east face of river arch 10, showing line of original access ramp on to river bridge (before repair)

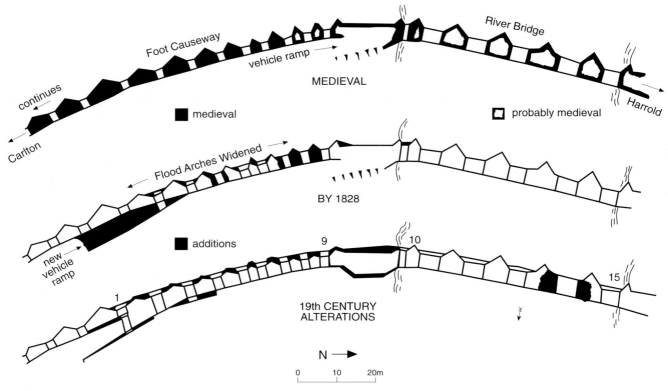

Fig 64 Harrold bridge: phase plan of river bridge and flood arches

Fig 65 Harrold bridge: flood arch 6 from west, showing successive widenings

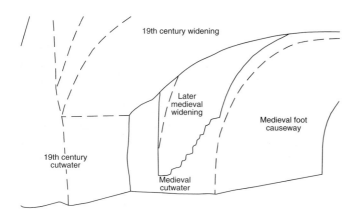

The date of this work is difficult to determine, as the stonework has no features characteristic of a particular period. The survey of c.1630 makes no distinctions among the thirty-one arches repaired by the County, but the purpose of the document is to record liabilities, not to provide a description of the bridge. A reference in 1757 to 'the new part of Harrold Bridge belonging to the County'[16] is suggestive, but there are no records in the earlier part of the 18th century to suggest substantial alterations. A late medieval or early post-medieval date is the closest that can be put forward.

The river bridge

The river arches display a great variety, in both style and constructional sequence, mostly reflecting the differing attitudes and responses of individual owners towards maintenance (Fig 66).

There is no great consistency in the widths of the arches. Before 1857, the bridge was at its narrowest at arches 11 and 12, being only 10 ft 4 in – 10 ft 6 in (3.15-3.20m), and the carriageway itself perhaps only 8 ft 10 in (2.70m) wide. Arches 13-15 were each 12 ft 5 in (3.79m) wide, and arch 10, 13 ft 1 in (3.99m) wide. The additional width of the end arches (10 and 15) may reflect the splaying out of the abutment at the bridge approaches.

The earliest phase of arch 10 may be contemporary with the early foot causeway. It was widened at an early date, from 13 ft 1 in (2.99m) to 14 ft 7 in (4.45m), by the addition of a stone skin against the upstream face. This may have occurred at the same time as the widening of the flood arches.

Fig 66 Harrold bridge: panoramic view of east face of river bridge (arches10-15)

Arch 11 is a pointed arch built in dressed ironstone with two orders of voussoirs, in contrast to the rounded limestone arches of the rest of the bridge. The style suggests that this is a late medieval replacement of an earlier arch. Its fine quality adds weight to the possibility that this arch, and the rest of the bridge and the causeway to the south, were once maintained by Harrold Priory.

The rest of the river bridge owes much of its appearance to post-medieval repairs and rebuilding. For example, at the Summer Assizes of 1667, the Dowager Countess of Peterborough was ordered to repair the 'third and fourth' arches (arches 13 and 12),[17] as part of her duties as lord of the manors of Carlton and Chellington (it is not clear which manor was responsible for which arch). Both arches were again out of repair in 1694.[18]

Arch 14, which had collapsed by 1532 (see above), was still spanned with timber beams in 1757:

'Arch belonging to Lord was started of and wished to be of stone as the two belonging to the other proprietors are but by placing beams across and attaching a strong prop underneath from the foundations to the centre of the arch it could last fifty years yet'.[19] The timber span is shown on an 1803 print by Thomas Hearne.[20]

19TH CENTURY DEVELOPMENTS

During the 18th and early 19th centuries regular small-scale work of an unspecified nature was carried out on the County parts of the bridge. Even so, the County was indicted in 1825 because the bridge was considered unsafe.[21] Soon afterwards, the bottom of the 'large arch' (arch 11) was pitched (that is, an invert inserted) and the top of the narrow causeway repaired.[22]

In 1826 the County Surveyor, Francis Giles, was ordered to examine the state of the bridge and to make recommendations for repairs or alterations. A detailed plan and east elevation survives from this period.[23] It shows that arch 14 was still spanned in timber, and that all the privately maintained arches (12 to 15) were fenced with posts and rails; by contrast, the County part of the river bridge (arches 10 and 11) had stone parapets (although a sketch drawing of 1825[24] indicates that the flood arches had a post and rail fence).

The earthen ramp which had given access to the river bridge before the flood arches were widened was still in position and unfenced. This was probably a major factor in the unsafe condition of the bridge, so in 1828 a retaining wall was built; this formed the passing bay which still survives.[25]

The following three decades saw a series of lengthy disputes between the County and local landowners over who was liable for repair. First, Earl de Grey was urged to replace his timber arch;[26] in response, he wrote to the Quarter Sessions (in 1840), refusing to repair it any longer.[27] Legal action followed and in 1844 judgment was found against him, requiring him to carry out repairs.[28]

However, consideration was given instead to a more radical solution. In 1847, the County offered to take over all remaining liabilities for Harrold bridge in return for contributions from the other owners towards a new iron bridge further downstream.[29] Earl de Grey and Mr Alston of Odell (who was responsible for arch 15) were prepared to consider the proposal. The Misses Trevor, whose estates in Carlton and Chellington had traditionally repaired arches 12 and 13, were less enthusiastic. In spite of further discussion, in 1849 they went so far as to deny all liability for arch 12.[30] Meanwhile the bridge continued to deteriorate, and in 1855 the County was required to defend itself at the Huntingdon Assizes against a presentment for failing to keep the bridge in repair.

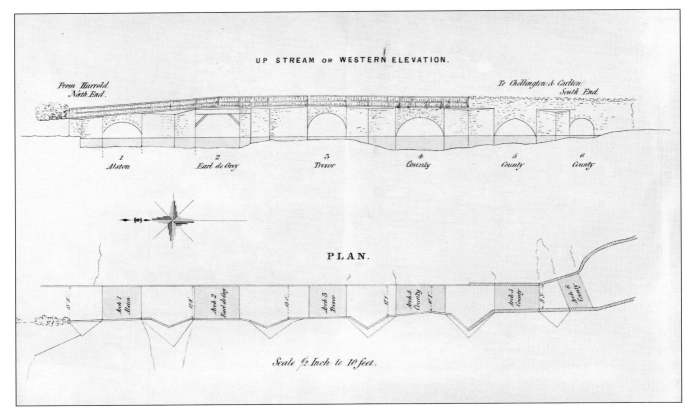

UP STREAM or WESTERN ELEVATION.

From Harrold
North End.

To Chellington & Carlton
South End.

1
Alston

2
Earl de Grey

3
Trevor

4
County

5
County

6
County

PLAN.

Scale ½ Inch to 10 feet.

Fig 67 Harrold bridge: plan and elevation of the river bridge in 1855, showing wooden railings and the timber span at arch 14 (Beds Record Office: QSX 19)

The Court found that the Misses Trevor, Earl de Grey and Mr Alston were liable for repairs to arches 13, 14 and 15 respectively, and the County responsible for the rest of the bridge.[31] A drawing which accompanied this judgment is reproduced in Figure 67.[32] The legal clarification provided the impetus that was needed for the bridge to be put in order. In 1856, Earl de Grey replaced his timber span with a semi-circular stone arch, which has double arch rings of squared limestone blocks. It had a wider carriageway than the adjacent arches, and the extent of the new work can still be seen in the gault brick copings which only occur over this arch. Early in 1857 the Quarter Sessions ordered that 'parapet walls be constructed on each side of the County portion of Harrold bridge in conformity with the new work lately completed by the

Earl de Grey'.[33] To achieve this, the bridge was widened on the west side in limestone, with brick arch rings springing from the existing cutwaters (Fig 68). The flood arches were also widened and the new limestone face was wrapped round the apex of the medieval triangular cutwaters, producing rounded buttress-type features (Fig 69). Traces of the earlier cutwaters were identified behind these buttresses during the course of modern stone repairs. In 1859, Mr Alston was recommended to make his arch (arch 15) the same width as the others.[34] This

Fig 68 Harrold bridge: west face of arches 11 and 12, showing 1857 widening

Fig 69 Harrold bridge: west face of flood arches, showing 1857 widening (arch 7 in the foreground was rebuilt in 1893)

Fig 70 Harrold bridge: remains of timber joist from railing, east face of bridge

work is slightly different from the widening of the rest of the bridge: it carries a brick string course, and the brick voussoirs have been rounded at the arris.

The 1857 widening saw the replacement of the old posts and rails which fenced most of the river bridge and flood arches. In some places on the east face, the butt-ends of the horizontal timber joists from this fence can still be seen below the present parapet (Fig 70).

Further campaigns of repair and alteration are recorded in the subsequent history of the bridge, including reinforcement of the first flood arch after serious damage by a traction engine in 1878.[35] In 1886 all the arches of the causeway were said to be in need of repair and the side-walls needed rebuilding. (This seems to have been accomplished simply by replacing the surface skin of stone: by 1992, when extensive repairs were undertaken, much of this old repair was pulling away from the main structure of the bridge and had to be rebuilt.) Arches 4, 16 and 17 of the causeway have been replaced in brick with stone arch rings; it is possible that this also dates from the repair work of 1886.

By 1892, there was a localised structural failure in the widening of flood arches 7 to 9.[36] This was remedied the following year[37] by rebuilding the west face of the arches; the extent of this work can clearly be seen in the distinctive ironstone arch rings and parapet copings (see Fig 69).

The remaining parts of the bridge in private hands were finally taken over by the County in 1930.[38]

NOTES

1 SP 955 565; HER 999; see also Peter McKeague, 'Harrold Bridge', *Beds Mag* 21 no 166, Autumn 1988, 234-237; Bedfordshire County Planning Department, '*Discovering our Past*' Broadsheet Series no 8, 'Harrold Bridge and Foot Causeway', Peter McKeague, 1988; *Lockgate* II no 3, Apr 1966, 37-41
2 *BHRS* 32, 1952, 12 no 1
3 *BHRS* 41, 1961, 88 no 204
4 *The Hundred Rolls for Bedfordshire,* 1274 and 1279, trans John S Thompson, Beds R O (unpub), 47 & 53
5 *Lockgate, op cit,* 39; *BHRS* 37, 1957, 64 no 203
6 *BHRS* 45, 1966, 52-53 no 112
7 *Lockgate, op cit,* 39; *BHRS* 37, 1957, 57 no 178d
8 Beds RO: ABP/R 3 f28r
9 *BHRS* 37, 1957, 80 no 254d
10 Beds RO: ABP/R 5 f40
11 Beds RO: L 26/573
12 Beds RO: P 27/1/5 Turvey
13 A J Foster, *A Tourist's Guide to Bedfordshire,* 1889, 46
14 Beds RO: TW 841
15 The line of this approach is still marked on a plan of c.1826 (Beds RO: PB 6/1)
16 Beds RO: QBM 1, 15
17 Beds RO: HSA 1667 S12
18 Beds RO: X 112/2
19 Beds RO: L 24/242
20 Beds RO: X 254/88/130
21 Beds RO: QBM 1, 157-158
22 Beds RO: QSR 27, 1825, 499
23 Beds RO: PB 6/1
24 Beds RO: GA 2/3
25 Beds RO: QBM 1, 1828, 217. A plan dated 1846, among the QSX 19 papers, shows two extra arches cut through what is now the passing bay, giving a total of eleven flood arches; no other documentary references, or physical evidence, for arches in this location survive
26 Beds RO: QBM 1, 295 (1835)
27 Beds RO: QBM 1, 295
28 Beds RO: QBM 1, 309-314
29 Beds RO: QBM 1, 322
30 Beds RO: QBM 1, 337
31 Beds RO: QBM 1, 383
32 Beds RO: QSX 19
33 Beds RO: QBM 1, 387-388
34 Beds RO: QBM 1, 409
35 Beds RO: QBP 2
36 Beds RO: Hi C M 2, 37-39
37 Beds RO: *ibid,* 71
38 Beds RO: CRT 130 HARR 8 – A summary history of Harrold Bridge by Record Office staff

TURVEY BRIDGE

Spanning the County boundary with Buckinghamshire, Turvey bridge is now maintained by Bedfordshire County Council for the Department of Transport.[1] The present bridge has eleven arches (numbered from the Buckinghamshire bank) with pointed cutwaters on the upstream (south) face between arches 1 and 2, and arches 5 to 10. There are no cutwaters on the downstream face. Seven arches carry the road over the more easterly main channel of the river, 154-161 ft (47-49m) wide; another four span the west channel, 62-66 ft (19-20m) wide. The two bridge sections are linked by a 89 ft (27m) long raised road causeway, and a further causeway crosses the flood plain on the Buckinghamshire side. The total length of the bridge is 686 ft (209m). The overall width is about 33 ft (10m).

Repairs to the bridge were carried out between 1991 and 1994 by the County Engineer for the Department of Transport.

Fig 71 Turvey bridge: from the south-east, c.1929 (Beds Record Office: Hi PH 20/1/1)

EARLY HISTORY

There is no mention of a bridge here before 1136/38 when Sampson Fortis granted '2 acres of meadow next Turveie Bridge' to Harrold Priory.[2] In 1272, justices travelling from Northampton stopped at the bridge and heard four cases on their way to Bedford[3] (perhaps at a predecessor of the Three Fishes).

The bridge was furnished with a chapel by the beginning of the 15th century, probably founded to provide an income from alms for repair work. In 1401/2, the monastic account roll of Harrold Priory, under its entries for Turvey, mentions '1lb wax of the tithe of the chapel upon the bridge'.[4] It is described as a 'hermitage and chapel' four years later in the records of the Bishop of Ely,[5] but is otherwise unrecorded. It seems to have disappeared before the inquiry into Chantry Chapels in Edward VI's reign, where no mention can be found.[6]

Some 16th century wills indicate that part of the bridge consisted of a long foot causeway on the Buckinghamshire side of the river. In 1522, Thomas Knight of Bedford left 10s for repairing 'the long bridge beyond Turvey bridge'.[7] In 1560 John, first Lord Mordaunt, bequeathed £40 to the inhabitants of Turvey for repairing the part of the bridge in Bedfordshire, and a further £26 13s 4d towards the repair of the 'long bridge' in Buckinghamshire, which was maintained by the parishes of Hardmead, Astwood, Lavendon, Newton Blossomville and Brayfield.[8]

A c.1630 survey of bridges in Willey Hundred recorded 'four high arches' in Bedfordshire, of which the Lord Mordaunt maintained one and the inhabitants of Turvey the remainder.[9] It makes no reference to the part of the bridge that lay in Buckinghamshire.

THE MEDIEVAL BRIDGE

The Foot Causeway

The foot causeway is shown on a map of Turvey in 1783[10] and of Lavendon and Brayfield in 1801.[11] The first description dates from 1824, when Theed Pearse, the Clerk of the Peace for the County of Bedfordshire, wrote:

'an ancient stone bridge over the River at Turvey and on the Buckingham side it is joined by an ancient horse and footbridge in Brayfield with several openings covered with planks to admit the passage of water in times of flood, to the repair of which several parishes are liable ...'[12]

According to John Higgins of Turvey Abbey, it had twenty-two planked arches and two stone ones. One arch, known as the Abbot's arch, was not the responsibility of the nearby parishes;[13] this may suggest a connection with the nearby Lavendon Abbey.

Fig 72 Turvey bridge: remains of foot causeway

When the causeway was demolished in 1828, Higgins recorded that one small section was left standing 'as a memorial, and picturesque object from the road'.[14] The ruins of this section, consisting of one of the two stone arches and a length of causeway on either side, can still be seen in the meadow south of the modern road (Fig 72). The springing and a few detached voussoir stones indicate that it was a small pointed arch. The east end is very broken down, perhaps the site of the second stone arch. To the west it is square-ended, presumably marking the start of the 'clapper' bridge. The overall width seems to have been about 7 ft (2.1m). Slight earthwork traces of several more pier bases survive alongside the roadside ditch to the south-west. The foot causeway is directly aligned with arches 3 and 4 of the river bridge, to which it originally gave access. Vehicles approached along an adjacent road which rose up to join the bridge at arch 3.

There was no foot causeway on the Turvey side, although a number of early 19th century illustrations show a raised stone footpath on the north side of the road.[15]

The River Bridge

In its early form, the river bridge consisted of the '4 high arches' over the east channel (probably arches 5 to 8), described in the survey of c.1630, and two arches (3 and 4) over what was originally the much smaller western channel on the county boundary. While arches 9 and 10 are of similar style to arches 5 to 8 they may date from after 1630.

The earliest arches to survive in near original form, though now much repaired, are 5 and 6 (Fig 76); they are pointed with a double order of thin limestone rubble voussoir stones. The other pointed arches (3, 8 and 9) all have a single arch ring of dressed limestone blocks with slight chamfers to the arrises. These seem to be repairs, especially as arch 8 has faint traces of an earlier rubble arch ring near the crown. The rounded arches (4, 7 and 10) are similarly repairs (see below).

The piers of the main river bridge are of typical local medieval style, with triangular cutwaters on the upstream face only. None of these cutwaters would have provided a suitable footing for the bridge chapel, which must have therefore been located either on the island or at the end of the bridge.

The original width of the carriageway was about 14 ft (4.25m).

POST-MEDIEVAL IMPROVEMENTS

The Bedford to Olney Turnpike Trust was founded by Act of Parliament in 1753/54[16]. It seems that the Trust soon undertook improvements to the western approach, raising the road by the construction of a low causeway. Certainly by 1824, the foot causeway (according to Theed Pearse) had been 'in a great measure superseded by a low modern carriage bridge or causeway running parallel with the latter bridge made by the Turnpike Trustees.'[17]

In severe floods in 1795, the 'fourth arch' (no 7) collapsed,[18] and there followed some debate as to who was liable for repairs. The Mordaunt estate, previously responsible, had been sold off to various members of the Higgins family in 1786, part going to John Higgins who became Lord of the Manor. It was determined that the

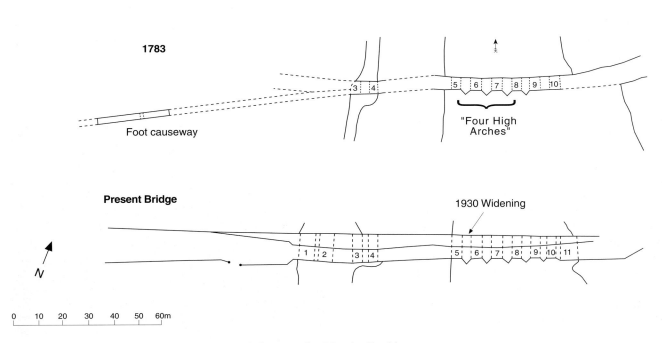

Fig 73 Turvey bridge: phase plan (original drawing by Martin Cook)

64

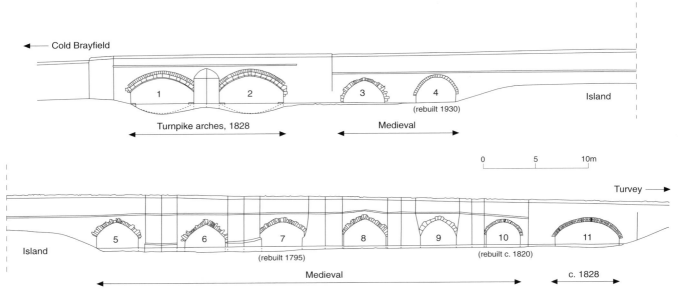

Fig 74 Turvey bridge: outline drawing of south elevation

Fig 75 Turvey bridge: the main river bridge from the south-east

Fig 76 Turvey bridge: south face of arches 5 and 6

owners of the former Mordaunt lands were still responsible for the bridge, so the Higgins family rebuilt the arch, and in about 1820 joined with the Turnpike Trust and the parish to rebuild arch 10.[19]

Further flood damage in 1823[20] led to another court case, and a useful sketch of the bridge made in 1824 is preserved among the papers.[21] Part of the foot causeway is shown, annotated 'Long Foot & Horse Bridge the openings covered with Boards washed away & impassable'. A larger timber span with 'A Flat Boarded Top' joined the causeway to the main bridge just west of arch 3. Both the causeway and the timber span are shown as having timber rails. Arches 3 to 10 have a plain string course and stone parapet above. The parapet (which survives today) had probably been built in the previous few years. It is certainly not original, as it sits awkwardly over some of the arches. In particular the string course is corbelled out over arch 9, and rises over the crown of arch 8. Also the square-sectioned string course extends over arch 10, which had recently been rebuilt.[22] The eastern (Turvey) approach had timber rails; a small culvert was shown on the 1824 plan, but this was replaced not long afterwards with a broad elliptical arch (arch 11).

In 1828, the Turnpike Trust 'constructed the present carriage roadway ... with flood arches under it and especially two large flood arches [arches 1 and 2] which were united to the west end of Turvey bridge ... but no part of the natural stream passes under these flood arches'.[23] The old causeway, which had joined the medieval bridge at the point where the new Turnpike arches were built, was dismantled at the same time,[24] and a small side arch constructed to give access from the new causeway to the meadow to the south.

Arches 1 and 2 have a four-centred shallow profile, with a double order of voussoirs, the lower composed of long stones set below the arch soffits (Fig 77). A pointed cutwater with a curved top separates the two arches on the upstream elevation. The spandrel walls are in ashlar limestone with a moulded string course above. The new work joined the existing bridge at the County boundary, emphasised by a sharp change in alignment. Although these

Fig 77 Turvey bridge: south face of arches 1 and 2

arches were originally built as dry flood arches, they now span the main body of the river.

More improvements to the Buckinghamshire end of the bridge were made in 1879, when retaining walls and parapets were built, and post and rail fences were added to the approaches.[25] This work was carried out at the instigation of the Buckinghamshire Quarter Sessions who had assumed responsibility for the western approach road from the Turnpike Trust. On the south side, the new retaining wall was not tied in firmly with the earlier accommodation arch which gave access to the meadow; this led to increasing instability, which was rectified in 1994. The footings of the 1879 north retaining wall can still be seen below the later stone wall associated with the widening of the bridge in 1930.

In 1881, the Bedfordshire Quarter Sessions resolved that the County should henceforth be responsible for maintenance of the Bedfordshire section of the bridge.[26]

THE 1930 WIDENING

The whole bridge was widened along its downstream (north) side in 1930 to about 33 ft (10m). In 1933, H C Griffin of The Council for the Preservation of Rural England described the work in a letter to *The Times*:

'... it is a matter of public interest that this ancient and beautiful bridge has not been debased by the present widening. Its character has been most carefully preserved in the process, even the old stones and watercourses being replaced in their original positions.'

Fig 78 Turvey bridge: north face during widening works, 1930

NOTES

1 SP 938 523; HER 1000; see also Peter McKeague & Martin Cook, 'Turvey Bridge', *Beds Mag* 22 no 173, Summer 1990, 206-209; Bedfordshire County Planning Department, *'Discovering our Past' Broadsheet Series* no 15, 'Turvey Bridge', Martin Cook, 1991; *Lockgate* I no 16, Jul 1965, 272-274; II no 1, Oct 1965, 2

2 *BHRS* 17, 1935, 16 no 2

3 *BHRS* 17, 1935, footnote on p188

4 *BHRS* 49, 1970, 43

5 *BHRS* 57, 1978, 20, quoting the Register of the Bishop of Ely, G/1/3, f205

6 See J E Brown, *Chantry Certificates for Bedfordshire*, nd

7 Beds RO: ABP/R 2, no 95, f90v

8 Beds RO: P 27/1/5, copy of extract in Turvey parish register; *Lockgate* I no 16, Jul 1965, 273

9 Beds RO: P 27/1/5

10 Beds RO: MA 3

11 Bucks RO: IR/25 AR

12 Beds RO: QSX 18; *Lockgate* I no 16, Jul 1965, 274

13 Beds RO: Mic 84 (John Higgins' scrapbook), p112

14 *ibid*

15 eg Beds RO: Z 102/88, c.1820

16 27 Geo II (copy in Beds RO: Z 417/36)

17 Beds RO: QSX 18

18 Beds RO: QSX 18; BC 529, T O Marsh papers; *Lockgate* I no 16, Jul 1965, 272;

19 Beds RO: QSX 18; *Lockgate* I no 16, Jul 1965, 272
20 Beds RO: BC 536, T O Marsh papers
21 Beds RO: QSX 18
22 Beds RO: QSX 18
23 Bucks RO: Q/AB 3/3
24 Beds RO: Mic 84, p112
25 Bucks RO: Q/AB 3/7-3/16
26 Beds RO: QSM 47, 1881, 283

SOME OTHER OUSE VALLEY BRIDGES

MEDIEVAL

Several medieval bridges across tributaries of the Great Ouse are known only from documentary evidence, often wills. William Slade of **Pertenhall** left bequests for the repair of bridges in the parish in 1508: 'to **Filbrigge** 2s; to **the bridge of the vill** 2s; to the bridge called **Walcard** 2s".[1] In **Stagsden,** Stephen Coxe in 1593 left 1s each for the repair of **Wickend bridge, 'Hellingreene bridge'** and **'Beerye meade bridge'.**[2] Wickend bridge[3] lay on the Bromham-Stagsden road, near the Wick End turn, and was later repaired by the Turnpike Trust.[4] It was recorded as a single stone arch in 1888[5] but has since been replaced by a modern structure. The location of Hellingreene bridge[6] is unknown, but the Tithe Apportionment map of 1876 locates 'Bury Mead furlong' adjacent to the bridge on the road from Stagsden to Kempston West End.[7] This is now a simple semi-circular limestone arch, probably dating from soon after the enclosure of the parish in 1828; there is a similar arch at Church End, which is likely to be of the same period.[8]

Other bridges are mentioned in rather more unfortunate circumstances. **Henry Patun's bridge** in Riseley[9] is known only from a hearing before justices in 1247, when a man claimed he had been attacked in 'a meadow between Hen Patun's bridge in Risele and the parson's croft'.[10] An inquest in 1279 heard that Joan, a poor child aged 5, went through Riseley to beg for bread, came to a bridge called 'Fordebrugge' and, as she tried to cross it, fell into the water and drowned.[11]

In 1276, an inquest into the death of a man in Elstow heard that 'about midnight on 17 May Osbert le Wuayl son of William Crustemasse of Elstow, who was drunk and disgustingly overfed, came from Bedford from door to door towards his house, which was on the north of Elstow bridge. When he arrived at his house he had the falling sickness, fell upon a stone on the right side of his head, breaking the whole of his head, and died by misadventure.'[12] The character of the medieval Elstow bridge is not known, but a 1767 map of Elstow[13] gives some insight into the importance that was placed on access across watercourses in later times. Where the Elstow Brook divides into two as it crosses the main street, and spreads out across the road, what appears to be a timber walkway is shown running for about 135 yards (123m) from one side of the water to the other.

Ketel bridge in Stagsden is recorded in several different sources.[14] Its first mention is as a landmark defining property belonging to Newnham Priory sometime before 1180.[15] In 1227, 'three Jews fell from a certain cart into the water at Ketelbrigg at Stacheden and were drowned'.[16] It was also recorded as a placename in 1426.[17]

Bedford was well supplied with small bridges, as well as the main bridge in the centre of the town. Speed's map of 1610 shows bridges on the three main roads entering the south of the town where they crossed the King's Ditch. Though none survive today, they stood at the west end of Cauldwell Street,[18] at Wilmer's Corner (now the St John's roundabout)[19] and at the east end of Cardington Road (formerly Potter Street). This last was named by Speed as **Talps bridge,** and may be that referred to in a will of 1368, which mentioned '... messuage [dwelling-house] in Potterstrate adjoining ... **Barrebrigg'.**[20]

Other bridges shown by Speed crossed the Saffron Ditch, which flowed through the north-west part of the town into the Ouse west of the main bridge. These were at the west end of Horne Lane[21] and in Midland Road (formerly Well Street).[22]

Remains of a footbridge across Elstow Brook were uncovered during excavations south of Elstow Abbey in the 1960s. There were two stone abutments on opposite sides of the stream, comprising limestone slabs held together by yellow sandy mortar.[23] The southern abutment was re-examined during excavations in 1995, when a second bridge was also identified further west. This had evidence of a triangular cutwater on the upstream face, and was dated by associated pottery to the 13th century.[24]

MILL BRIDGES

While it can be assumed that most medieval watermills were associated with small bridges, few are specifically mentioned in documents. The references which do occur tend to be post-medieval in date.

Downstream of Bedford, at **Castle Mills,** Risinghoe, the antiquary John Leland crossed the River Ouse in the early 1530s by wooden bridges over the two river channels.[25] Doubtless this crossing had existed for many years before, though it was never a public highway.[26]

Coney bridge, Felmersham is mentioned in perambulation of Felmersham parish in 1608.[27] Further upstream, notes by Rev Thomas Orlebar Marsh record: 'Great Flood attended with a great Storm, Thurs night 30th Oct 1823. Odell wooden Bridge carried away'.[28] This was probably a structure associated with Odell mill.[29] In 1814, Lord St John of Bletsoe was indicted for failing to repair 'a common public foot Bridge commonly called Stoke Mills Bridge [near Sharnbrook] over a Stream of Water called the Back Brook'.[30]

POST-MEDIEVAL

Minor roads and tracks in the upper Ouse valley still carry some small limestone bridges, in traditional style though probably not of any great age. **Park Gate bridge** in Village Road, **Bromham** is a 19th century limestone rubble bridge with dressed arches.[31] **Park Lane bridge** in **Sharnbrook** is shown on Jefferys' map of 1765. It is now a coursed limestone bridge of three small arches with plain voussoirs. The piers, which have no cutwaters, have been set in concrete.[32] It stands on the site of 'Clevehogs' (or 'Clenehogs') bridge, recorded in 1563.[33]

In some cases, however, even small local bridges were designed by architects. **Wootton Broadmead bridge,** which was funded by the parish, was designed by 'Mr Wing of Bedford' and built in 1845;[34] this was presumably James Tacy Wing, the son of John Wing who built Bedford bridge.[35] It was a single-arched brick bridge, with wing walls which had decorative brick features. There were iron railings rather than a parapet. It was demolished in 1988.

The first bridge built by the modern County Council was at Salph End, Renhold. It was opened on 28th July 1892[36] but has been replaced by a broad concrete culvert.

NOTES

1 HER 15731 (Filbrigge); 15732 (Walcard bridge); Patricia Bell, 'Bedfordshire Wills, 1480-1519', *BHRS* 45, 1966, p94 no 186
2 Beds RO: CRT 130 Stagsden 5 – Notes on Timsell bridge, made by Record Office staff
3 SP 988 495; HER 15752
4 Beds RO: QBP 3
5 Beds RO: QBP 9
6 HER 15753
7 SP 986 488; HER 15754; Beds RO: MAT 40/2
8 SP 980 492; HER 15769; Beds RO: MA 53, Book M
9 HER 12629
10 *BHRS* 21, 1939, 158 no 640
11 HER 12630; *BHRS* 41, 1961, 82 no 187
12 TL 050 473; HER 15700; *BHRS* 41, 1961, 97-98 no 240
13 Beds RO: X 1/6/1
14 HER 15755
15 *BHRS* 43, 1964, 254 no 562
16 *BHRS* 3, 1916, 172
17 R F White, *Stagsden Parish Survey,* unpub, 1976 (copy in Heritage Group, County Hall)
18 TL 049 493; HER 15683
19 TL 051 491; HER 15682
20 TL 054 493; HER 15681; Beds RO: FN 349
21 TL 048 496; HER 15684
22 TL 047 497; HER 15685
23 TL 049 473; HER 262; Baker D, 'Excavations at Elstow Abbey, Bedfordshire, 1968-70: Third interim report', *Beds Archaeol J* 6, 1971, 55-64,64,64, see pp 63-64
24 Michael Dawson & David Fell, 'Excavations at Elstow Abbey, 1995', *Beds Archaeology* 22, 1996, 129-146, see pp 133 & 136
25 Toulmin Smith L (ed), *John Leland's Itinerary in England & Wales,* London, 1964, vol 1, 101
26 TL 092 508; HER 336
27 Beds RO: CRT 130 FELM 3, quoted in Draycott W E, *Grain and chaff, thrashing out the history of Felmersham, Bedfordshire,* 1986, 15
28 Beds RO: BC 536, T O Marsh papers
29 ?SP 966 576; HER 15729
30 TL 011 590; HER 15744; Beds RO: QBM 1, 69
31 TL 007 507; HER 10167
32 SP 996 597; HER 14980
33 Beds RO: AD 997, p143
34 TL 019 437; HER 15763; Beds RO: P 3/8/1, Vestry Minutes
35 H Colvin, *A Biographical Dictionary of British Architects, 1600-1840,* London, 1978, 906
36 Beds RO: Hi C M2, p46

THE IVEL AND FLIT VALLEYS

The River Ivel rises in Hertfordshire and joins the River Great Ouse at Tempsford. It has several main tributaries, of which the most notable are the River Flit which flows eastwards across mid-Bedfordshire, and the River Hiz. It is narrower than the Ouse and does not have the same broad flood plain, so its bridges are smaller in scale, but there were nonetheless a number of important crossings in medieval times (see Figs 5 and 6). Bridges carrying the Great North road over the Ivel at Girtford and Biggleswade are first documented in the 12th and early 13th centuries, but others existed on lesser roads at Blunham, Langford, Henlow (Stockbridge) and Arlesey. On the River Flit, 16th century references to Clifton, Shefford and Clophill bridges suggest that they had been built some time before. Of these medieval bridges only Arlesey, and the fine bridge at Sutton, survive.

Blunham bridge was rebuilt probably in the 17th century, and in the 18th century, older bridges were replaced with new at Girtford, Biggleswade, Chicksands and Clophill. There was frequent repair and rebuilding during the 19th century, mainly by the County Quarter Sessions, and bridges at Potton and Flitwick are among the first bridges built by the modern County Council in the late 19th century.

The 19th century bridges of the Ivel Navigation (and the associated King's bridge in Southill) are discussed in a separate section below.

BLUNHAM RIVER BRIDGE

Blunham river bridge has five stone arches and carries a minor road towards Tempsford over the main channel of

Fig 79 Blunham bridges: location plan

the River Ivel. While it is probably of early post-medieval date, it is of typical medieval style.[1]

HISTORY

Very little is known about Blunham bridge's early history. Hugh the Cobbler drowned in 1270 whilst trying to cross it, when 'he slipped and fell upon the ice, which broke, and drowned by misadventure'; this implies that there was no parapet or rail at that time.[2] The present stone

Fig 80 Blunham river bridge: from the south

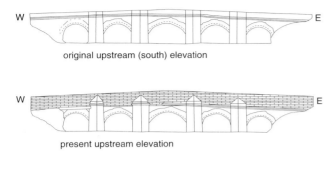

original upstream (south) elevation

present upstream elevation

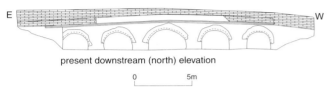

present downstream (north) elevation

0   5m

Fig 81 Blunham river bridge: phase drawing

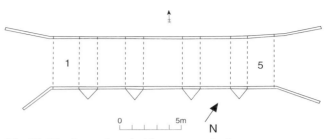

0   5m   N

Fig 82 Blunham river bridge: ground plan

Fig 83 Blunham river bridge: invert, arch 5

structure is probably much later, of 17th century origin. It is first shown on an estate map of 1719.[3]

The Quarter Sessions concluded in 1828 that the bridge was at least 200 years old and that the parish had been solely responsible for its upkeep,[4] although it was not known who had first built it. It was adopted as a county bridge in 1839.[5]

A major scheme of repairs was undertaken by the County Engineer in 1992.

STRUCTURAL EVIDENCE

Blunham bridge is of sandstone and consists of five rounded arches, with broad chamfers which suggest a 17th century date;[6] this is consistent with the Quarter Sessions' estimate for the age of the bridge in 1828. Each arch has a keystone, flanked on most of the arches by other slightly projecting stones at the crown. The piers have triangular cutwaters on the upstream faces only, which originally would have risen in medieval style to the road level, forming pedestrian refuges (Fig 81). There was, perhaps, a low stone parapet above the moulded string course, traces of which may still be seen on the downstream face. At some stage the parapet was raised in height, the refuges infilled, and the cutwaters finished off with the present half-pyramid capstones.[7] Blue Staffordshire copings and stone terminal caps were introduced in 1866,[8] and reused when a further 15 in (380mm) of brickwork was added to the parapets in 1893.[9] Other alterations have included strengthening or rebuilding all the abutments except that to the south-east.

During recent repair works, a well-preserved paved stone invert was recorded under the east arch (arch 5); it may be contemporary with the construction of the bridge (Fig 83).

NOTES

1   TL 155 518; HER 997; see also Peter McKeague, 'Blunham Bridges', *Beds Mag* 21 no 168, Spring 1989, 333-336
2   *BHRS* 41, 1961, 28 no 61
3   Beds RO: L 33/286 f50
4   Beds RO: QBM 1, 223, 225-6; QBP 1, 1828
5   Beds RO: QBM 1, 288
6   English Heritage, Scheduled Ancient Monument Record form
7   Similar examples may be seen on Wakerley bridge on the Welland (Jervoise, 1931, fig 31) and on Ketton bridge on the Chater (*ibid,* fig 33), both in Northamptonshire
8   Beds RO: QBC 3
9   Beds RO: Hi C M 2, p63

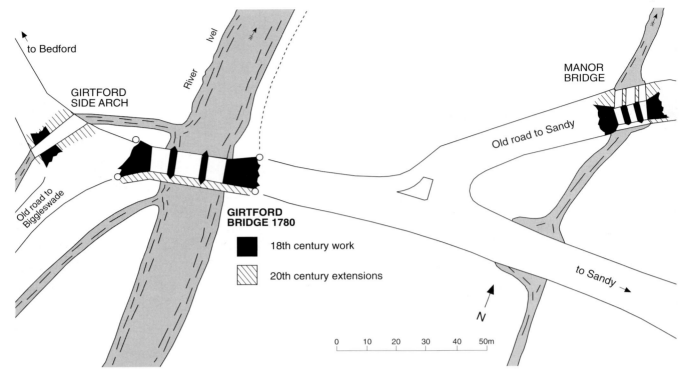

Fig 84 Girtford bridge: location plan

GIRTFORD BRIDGE

This three-arched bridge formerly carried the Great North road over the River Ivel, and still carries the Bedford to Sandy road. It is a fine, relatively unaltered, example of a late 18th century masonry bridge.[1]

HISTORY

Earlier bridges

The crossing dates back to long before the present bridge was built. 'Grutford' or gravel ford is first recorded in 1247,[2] whilst the 'pontem (bridge) de Gretteford' features as a boundary in a 13th century charter of Newnham Priory.[3] A bridge is clearly mentioned in 1504 when 3s 4d was left towards its repair in the will of Ralph Brunsale of Sandy.[4] Ogilby's 1675 route map from Oxford to Cambridge marks 'Gatford Stone bridge' to the west of Sandy,[5] though his London-St Neots map shows 'a Wood bridge'.[6]

In 1725 the road north from Biggleswade to Alconbury Hill, which crossed the Ivel at Girtford, was turnpiked,[7] and provisions were made in 1736 'for repairing and enlarging Girtford, Haile, and Diddington bridges'.[8] In 1756 work started on the first stage of the Ivel Navigation from its junction with the Ouse at Tempsford upstream to Biggleswade, but evidently the old bridge was not considered to be an obstruction for navigation traffic.

The 18th century bridge

John Wing of Rutland was commissioned to rebuild Girtford bridge by the Turnpike Trust. Wing's diary shows that work began on 16th May 1780 and on 10th November he struck the centre of the 'grate arch'.[9] He received his final payment from the trustees on 28th September 1782. He was paid £600 for his work, though other bills and material costs may have been paid separately.[10] The Rev Thomas Orlebar Marsh records that the bridge was built with stone from Sandy.[11]

An illustration by Thomas Fisher shows the completed bridge and a separate side arch to the west, perhaps only some twenty or thirty years after completion (Fig 85).[12]

There is very little of note in the bridge's subsequent history except numerous repairs and slight alterations. Although built by the Turnpike Trust, it was later main-

Fig 85 Girtford bridge: watercolour by Thomas Fisher (Luton Museum and Art Gallery)

Fig 86 Girtford bridge: from the north (Beds Photographic Services)

tained through the Quarter Sessions even during the life of the turnpike. The earliest Quarter Sessions records date from 1822,[13] and fairly frequent maintenance accounts were presented after that date.

When built, Girtford had a wide carriageway, and there has been no need to widen it. It was only in 1947 that increased traffic prompted the addition of a metal foot-bridge, cantilevered out from the south face of the bridge. In 1962 the bridge, and the awkward bend on which it lay, were by-passed by the dual carriageway to the east.

STRUCTURAL EVIDENCE

The bridge is built almost entirely of local sandstone. It is wide even by 18th century standards. Some 29 ft 6 in (9.0m) in overall width, it supports a 25 ft 6 in (7.8m) wide carriageway between the parapets. It has three flattened elliptical arches. The large centre arch is flanked by a lower arch on each side, but the bridge is asymmetrical, with the greater drop on the west side reflecting the height of the river bank. The arches are well-constructed

to a high standard of design, with regular dressed stone soffits and radial wedge-shaped voussoir stones. There is a prominent raised keystone, flanked by raised voussoirs on either side, at the crown of each arch.

The piers are much narrower than those of medieval bridges, reflecting advances in engineering skills during the 18th century. Cutwaters on both the upstream and downstream faces are capped by half-pyramids rising at the springings of the arches at water level. The steeply rising sandstone string course at the base of the stone parapets reflects the original hump-backed appearance of the bridge. Above the string course, the parapets are featureless except for projecting panels over the crown of the centre arch on both faces, and large round terminals.

Apart from the addition of the footbridge Girtford bridge is almost unaltered. The only other significant change has been the lessening of the gradient over the bridge by raising the road surface on the approaches and building up the parapet walls. This can easily be seen in the coursing of the parapets.

THE SIDE BRIDGES

Two nearby bridges at Girtford are also a part of the site's history.

To the east a three-arched bridge, known as Manor bridge, spans a side channel of the Ivel, but only the pier bases of the original bridge now survive.[14] The relatively narrow width of the surviving cutwaters on the upstream face suggest an 18th century date. An early postcard of this bridge[15] shows that it had brick parapets with half-round copings & stone terminals, with angled wing walls. There is a triangular refuge to the right (south). It is not clear how much of this was a later alteration. A 20th

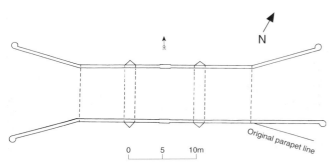

Fig 87 Girtford bridge: ground plan

century widening obscures the downstream elevation, but it seems to lack any protective cutwaters. The rounded arches were truncated at the springing by the present reinforced steel bridge deck in the mid-1930s.[16]

On the west there is a single span structure called Girtford side arch.[17] This is awkwardly placed at the junction of the Bedford to Sandy road with the old Great North road, and has been massively extended round an original single sandstone arch. Traces of decorative keystones can be detected on both elevations despite the later widenings. To the north there is a long concrete and steel culvert whilst a short brick arch has been abutted against the south face. No traces remain of the solid parapets shown by Fisher.

Despite differences in scale (both side bridges are almost 10 ft (3.0m) narrower than the main bridge) and variations in style, the three structures are probably broadly contemporary.

NOTES

1 TL 163 489; HER 2044; see also Peter McKeague, 'Girtford and Biggleswade Bridges', *Beds Mag* 22 no 169, Summer 1989, 12-14
2 Mawer and Stenton, 1926, 108
3 *BHRS* 43 pt 1, 1963, 3 no 1
4 *BHRS* 45, 1966, 41-2 no 91
5 Beds RO: Z 236/3
6 Beds RO: Z 236/2
7 11 Geo I, c20 (copy in Beds RO: Z 417/26)
8 9 Geo II (copy in Beds RO: T 47/19)
9 Beds RO: X 106/80
10 Beds RO: X 40/2
11 Beds RO: BC 534
12 Beds RO: Z 49/376, from a watercolour in Luton Museum
13 Beds RO: QBM 1, 130; QSR 25, 1822, 438
14 TL 164 491; HER 15742

15 W B Hanford, *Sandy in Old Picture Postcards*, 1986, 2. The original postcard is in Beds RO: X 758/1/11 no 140
16 Beds Co Surveyor's records, BR/A1/10-2 (1935)
17 TL 162 489; HER 15741

BIGGLESWADE BRIDGE

THE MEDIEVAL BRIDGE

The earliest occurrence of the name 'Pichelesuuade' (which means 'Bichel's ford') is in the Domesday Book of 1086.[1] There was a bridge here by the 14th century: in 1302 Bishop Dalderby of Lincoln gave indulgences to all those contributing to the repair of the bridge, and in July 1372 pontage was granted to the men of Biggleswade for three years.[2]

There are occasional references to the bridge in 17th century estate boundaries,[3] and Ogilby marks a stone bridge here on his London to St Neots route map of 1675.[4] The Merchant's Miscellany and Traveller's Compendium for 1785, Bedfordshire's earliest directory, described the structure as a 'good stone bridge'.[5]

In 1790, Viscount Torrington recorded: 'On the south side of Biggleswade Bridge is written: "The River Iyvell was made navigable in the year of Our Lord 1758"'.[6] This inscription was recovered when the later 18th century bridge was demolished.[7]

THE 18th CENTURY BRIDGE

In about 1796 the medieval bridge was replaced, the work being jointly financed by Trustees of the Biggleswade and

Fig 88 Biggleswade bridge: south face (Biggleswade Library)

Fig 89 Biggleswade bridge: north face (Co Engineer)

Alconbury Hill Turnpike, the Commissioners of the Ivel Navigation, and the County through the Quarter Sessions.[8] Local masons, Rivetts of Biggleswade, were employed under the supervision of Sir Philip Monoux.[9] The Rev Thomas Orlebar Marsh recorded that it was built with stone from Sandy.[10]

A much worn inscription, saved when the bridge was demolished in 1948, seems to record its construction:

'. . . . . .
widening of the . . . Commissioners . . .
of this Turnpike by . . . . .
. . . of the Commissioners
River Ivel Navigation . . .
by the County of Bedford
in the year of Our Lord 1796'[11]

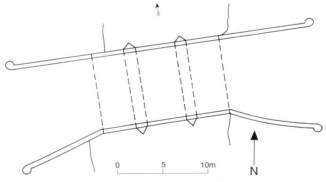

Fig 90 Biggleswade bridge: ground plan

Subsequent maintenance was carried out by the County. Despite the presence of the newly built bridge some traffic may have continued to use a ford alongside; in 1818 repairs were needed as one wing wall had been undermined by the wash from cattle and carriages going into the river at the watering place.[12]

Architecturally Biggleswade bridge was remarkably similar to John Wing's 1780 bridge at Girtford. Comparisons may be drawn between the three sandstone arches, the same overall width (29 ft 6 in, 9.00m), the narrow piers, the triple keystones, and the high stone parapets with a panel over the crown of the bridge. The Biggleswade arches were, however, rounded rather than elliptical. The triangular cutwaters rose to the arch springing where they terminated; on the upstream face they were capped by half pyramids as at Girtford, but downstream the tops were chamfered back to the face of the bridge. It is likely that the builders of Biggleswade bridge copied many of the features already seen in Girtford bridge a few miles downstream, but adapted the design to suit the site location.

Increased road traffic during the 20th century led first to the construction of a second bridge alongside in 1939-40, and then to the replacement of the old bridge in 1948. The modern structures are steel Callender Hamilton bridges, known locally as the 'Meccano bridges'.

74

NOTES
1 Mawer & Stenton, 1926, 100-101
2 *VCH Beds* 2, 1908, 209-210; *Cal Patent Rolls* 1370-74, 187; Jervoise, 1932, 94. The 'medieval bridge of three pointed arches' described in *VCH Beds* 2, 1908, 209 was not, however, this medieval structure but its successor of three semi-circular arches built in 1796; this misunderstanding is repeated in N Pevsner, *The Buildings of England: Bedfordshire and the County of Huntingdon and Peterborough,* 1968, 56
3 Beds RO: W 2593; CRT 100/5
4 Beds RO: Z 236/2
5 J F Henington, *The Merchants Miscellany and Travellers Compendium,* 1785, 17
6 Andrews C Bruyn (ed), *The Torrington Diaries,* vol 2, 1935, 287. The sketch opposite p290, labelled 'Biggleswade Bridge', is actually Bedford bridge, which he visited and described the following day
7 Beds RO: CRT 130 Biggleswade 7 – Notes on Stones from Old Biggleswade Bridge
8 TL 187 452; HER 14115; see also Peter McKeague, 'Girtford and Biggleswade Bridges, *Beds Mag* 22 no 169, Summer 1989, 12-14
9 Beds RO: QBM 1, 34; X 40/3
10 Beds RO: BC 534, T O Marsh papers
11 Beds RO: CRT 130 Biggleswade 7
12 Beds RO: QSR 23, 1818, 615

SUTTON BRIDGE

The narrow bridge at Sutton carries the village footpath over the small Potton brook alongside a ford.[1] It lies near the eastern boundary of the Ivel valley catchment area, well away from major watercourses and important highways. Archaeological recording was carried out before and during repair works in 1986.[2]

HISTORY

Very little is known historically about the bridge, which remained in private hands until 1941. It was first mentioned in 1504 when Thomas Loffe left 3s 4d towards its upkeep.[3] John Burgoyne, lord of Sutton manor, was more generous, leaving 40s towards repairs in 1540.[4] A charity was set up in the early 18th century from funds left by his descendants, John and Constance Burgoyne, for maintaining the church and the bridge, and for providing a school.[5] This arrangement rationalised previous manorial responsibilities for the bridge into a trust. No other party had any demonstrable involvement with the bridge until the County Council took over its maintenance in 1941.[6]

STRUCTURAL EVIDENCE

The bridge is of very simple design. Two pointed arches support the pathway. Each has a span measuring 9ft 10in (3.00m) in both width and height and they are separated by a central pier 4ft 7in (1.4m) wide. A triangular cutwater rises the full height of the bridge to form a pedestrian refuge on the upstream (north) face. Both upstream abutments are protected by splayed wall faces. In contrast the downstream face is comparatively plain.

Phase 1
Excavations revealed that the bridge had been built upon a timber foundation raft. Four elm beams were laid across the stream bed to form a level building platform for the abutments and pier. Radiocarbon determinations suggest a mid-13th century date for the felling of the timber and its subsequent use as a foundation soon after.[7]

The masonry is of a high standard, comprising dressed local sandstone laid in regular courses. The arches are

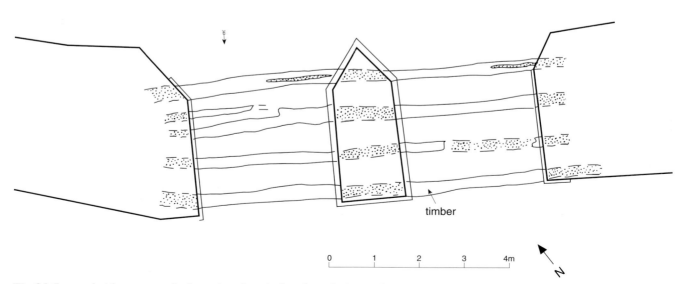

timber

0 1 2 3 4m

N

Fig 91 Sutton bridge: ground plan, showing timber foundation raft

Fig 92 Sutton bridge: timber foundation under west arch, during excavation

formed by a double order of dressed voussoir stones and even the soffits are of a high quality. As originally built, the bridge had a far more hump-backed appearance than now, with steep, perhaps even stepped approaches. There is unlikely to have been a parapet or railing though there was perhaps a slightly raised kerb.

Phase 2

At some stage the height of the bridge was reduced by truncating the crown of the upper order of voussoirs, and a string course supporting a parapet was added. Local sandstone was again used for this work, although it is of a noticeably darker hue and therefore probably from a different quarry. The approach ramps were extended, especially on the south face, with the effect of lessening the steepness of the bridge and making it easier and safer to cross.

Phase 3

A second alteration may be identified in areas of the bridge where re-used ashlar limestone has been incorporated. The wing walls and approach ramps were again extended to lessen the gradient of the ramp still further. Slight alterations and patch repairs were made to the south face, and much of the north-west wing wall dates from this phase. The plinths round the arch bases were probably also added.

The date of these works is unknown, but ashlar limestone may have become available either as a result of repairs to the church tower in 1686 (recorded in a datestone on the west face of the church tower), or of alterations at Sutton Park House in 1786 or its demolition in 1825.[8] The moulding on the bridge's limestone parapet copings is almost identical to that which can still be seen on the parish church.

DISCUSSION

The quality of Sutton bridge sets it apart from the other surviving medieval bridges in the county, its design and stonework being far superior to the sandstone bridges at Arlesey and Barford, for example. It was certainly not designed specifically for use by packhorses engaged in long distance trade, as there were never any important routes through the village, and local markets were better

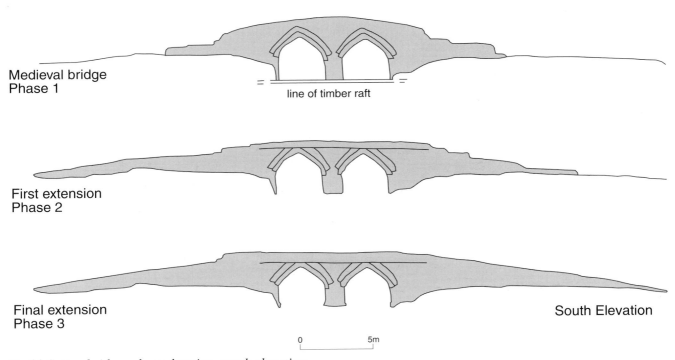

Medieval bridge
Phase 1

line of timber raft

First extension
Phase 2

Final extension
Phase 3

South Elevation

0   5m

Fig 93 Sutton bridge: phase drawing, south elevation

Fig 94 Sutton bridge: from the north (Beds Photographic Services)

served by other roads. Its origins are more likely to be associated with the creation of Sutton Park, when the village may have been deliberately moved from a position around the church to its present linear plan east of the stream. The bridge thus formed a fine (even ostentatious) landscape feature on the extreme edge of the new park, as well as linking the relocated village with the parish church and improving local communications between manorial lands.

Fig 95 Sutton bridge: from the south-east (Beds Photographic Services)

NOTES
1. TL 220 474; HER 511
2. A full account appears in P McKeague, 'Sutton Packhorse Bridge, *Beds Archaeology* 18, 1988, 64-80; see also Peter McKeague, 'Sutton Packhorse Bridge, *Beds Mag* 21 no 164, Spring 1988, 142-144 and Bedfordshire County Planning Department, *'Discovering our Past' Broadsheet Series* no 4, 'Repairing Sutton Packhorse Bridge', Peter McKeague, 1987
3. *BHRS* 37, 1957, 14, no 46d
4. *BHRS* 58, 1979, 154, no 119
5. *VCH Beds* 2, 1908, 250
6. Details of expenditure are given in the churchwardens' accounts (Beds RO: P 123/5/1-3)
7. HAR 8803, 790 +/- 40 BP; HAR 8804, 750 +/- 50 BP; see also McKeague, *Beds Archaeology* 1988, 80
8. Beds RO: CRT 130 Sutton 8 – Notes by C J Pickford on Sutton Park House

Fig 96 Tannery bridge, Potton: inside face of north parapet

TANNERY BRIDGE, Potton

Tannery bridge[1] which carries the Potton to Wrestlingworth road over Potton Brook dates from 1895.[2] It is contemporary with Flitwick bridge (see below), and these two bridges are the earliest built by the modern County Council to have survived.

It has a simple red-brick arch, but surprisingly decorative parapets. On the internal face, moulded grey bricks surround a small central panel (which on the north parapet carries a datestone). On either side are two larger panels, in which grey bricks are also used to pick out a pyramid design. A broad triangular coping is supported by a further moulded course, above a row of bricks decorated with pyramidal studs. The square terminals bear limestone caps with a triangular pediment on each face.

NOTES
1. TL 225 490; HER 10681
2. Beds RO: Hi C M 2, pp285 & 330

BROOM BRIDGE, Southill

Crossing an old channel of the River Ivel which forms the boundary between Southill and Biggleswade,[1] a bridge

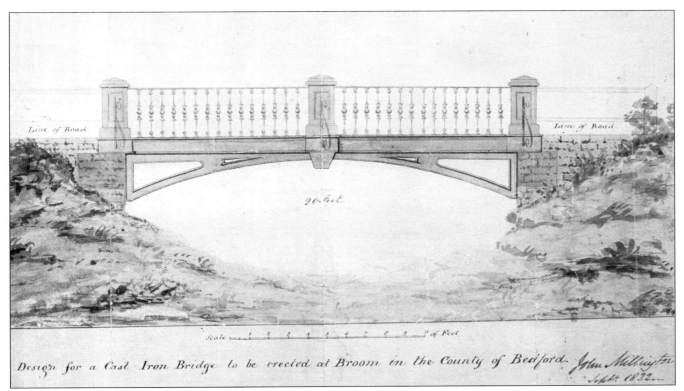

Fig 97 Broom bridge, Southill: design drawing by John Millington, 1823 (Beds Record Office: PB 3/1)

known as Broom bridge collapsed in about 1788 and was rebuilt in brick by the inhabitants of Broom in the parish of Southill.[2] It was replaced in 1823 with an iron bridge designed by John Millington, the County Surveyor. The ironwork, made by Lees Cottam and Co of Coalbrookdale in Shropshire, was brought by canal, unloaded at Linford wharf on the Grand Junction Canal near Newport Pagnell, and brought overland to the site for assembly. Accounts surviving in the Quarter Sessions records show that the ironwork cost £13 per ton; inclusive of screws, bolts and other wrought ironwork, the making of the drawings, and the expense of carriage from Coalbrookdale to Linford, the bill came to £156 16s 0d. The bridge itself weighed 12 ton 1 cwt 1 stone and 12 lbs (12.25 tonnes). A further £22 9s 10d was incurred in transporting the ironwork from Stanton Hill wharf (near Linford) to Broom.[3]

The bridge was a simple single span twenty feet wide. From Millington's drawing it appears to have been formed by a series of iron girders resting on brick abutments. The braced girders supported a flat road surface, with two cut-outs in each spandrel. There was a low relief 'keystone' which projected below the 'arch ring'. There were ornamental iron railings above, ending in square stone terminals. The design included stone pillars over the 'keystones' in the centre of the arch, but these do not appear to have been constructed.

On the 18th February 1873, a 10 to 12 ton traction engine (Fowler's of Leeds) fell through the arch, all but destroying the bridge. Contemporary newspaper reports and photographs survive, giving some indications of the character of the bridge.[4]

NOTES
1 TL 183 430; HER 15750
2 Beds RO: P 69/21/1 – account book of Southill's Surveyor of Highways
3 Beds RO: PB 3; QBM 1, 137-138
4 Beds RO: Z 49/594-595; *Beds Times*, 18.2.1873

LANGFORD BRIDGE

Langford bridge, on the River Hiz between Langford and Henlow,[1] was first described in 1817 after it was badly damaged in floods. A report to the Quarter Sessions recorded it as 'an ancient Structure consisting of 2 Gothic Arches supported upon a center pier 4 ft 6 in [1.4m] wide'. About a quarter of the bridge had fallen away, reducing the width to about 9 ft (2.75m).[2] The description and dimensions compare closely with Arlesey bridge further upstream and suggest that it was of medieval origin. A bridge is marked here on Jefferys' County Map of 1765.

The Quarter Sessions produced evidence that repairs had been carried out by the Langford's Surveyor of the Highways in recent years,[3] but in 1818 accepted liability for providing a new bridge.[4] John Millington, the County

Surveyor, proposed a simple timber bridge resting on brick abutments,[5] but in 1819 the decision was made to erect an iron bridge.[6] It was cast by Lees and Co at Coalbrookdale and transported in pieces by canal to Linford wharf on the Grand Junction Canal west of Newport Pagnell.[7] The sections were then carried overland to Langford for assembly at the site. The bridge was completed at a cost of £254 8s 8d in 1819.[8]

Proposals were made to widen the bridge 'like Arlsey' in 1851,[9] though it is doubtful if a single span brick arch was added alongside the existing ironwork. Three additional wrought iron solid flange girders were fixed in 1873 to lend support to the iron plates of the deck,[10] following the collapse of the iron bridge at Broom.

The bridge was taken down in 1946, but photographs of the demolition works record its character.[11] The iron girders were slightly curved, with cut outs in the spandrels. The girder on the upstream face was elaborately decorated, with a 'keystone' in relief bearing faint traces of a date '1819'. A commemorative inscription recording the makers was also visible below a raised band, but cannot be deciphered. The abutments show evidence of widening, which may have been part of the work carried out in 1873. They were part brick and part sandstone with a straight joint between. It is unclear which section was earlier; the 'commemorative' girder is situated above the brickwork, but may have been moved when the bridge was widened.

NOTES
1 TL 182 401; HER 15709
2 Beds RO: QSR 23, 1817, 296 – report by John Millington, 15.4.1817
3 Beds RO: QSR 23, 1817, 295
4 Beds RO: QBM 1, 108
5 Beds RO: QSR 23, 1817, 296
6 Beds RO: QBM 1, 113
7 Beds RO: QSR 24, 1819, 434
8 Beds RO: QSR 24, 1819, 367
9 Beds RO: QBM 1, 349
10 Beds RO: QBP 4, 1873
11 Photographs held by County Engineer

Fig 98 Langford bridge: under demolition, 1946 (Co Engineer)

ARLESEY BRIDGE

Rising in Hertfordshire, the River Hiz enters Bedfordshire at Arlesey and joins the Ivel on the Langford parish boundary. In the medieval period it seems that there was only one road crossing of this river, at Church End, Arlesey. The medieval bridge still stands alongside the 1960s flyover.[1] Its significance was identified in the course of research into other bridges in April 1988.

EARLY HISTORY

Documentation is sparse, but there are references in medieval manorial records. The surname 'Brygge' appears in documents of 1378/79, perhaps indicating the presence of a bridge.[2] 'Scotelfordbrugg' is mentioned in 1396/97, when Abbot William of Waltham Abbey granted one rood of land to John Fechale,[3] and 'Scottfordbrige' occurs in 1498/99.[4] There was evidently a second bridge built in the parish, as one rood of land at 'Newbrigge' is listed in 1466/67.[5] Associated holdings suggest that 'Scotelfordbrigge' lay in the south field, so the surviving bridge may be the one known as 'Newbrigge'. It was therefore probably built sometime before the mid-15th century, and was certainly standing by the time of the 1566 survey of Etonbury Manor which held land bounding the site:

'... iij [3] acres of ground boundinge of Saynt Andrews Chappell on the North East and the Stone Bridge on the South west'[6]

PHASE 1

The original bridge is built from local sandstone and consists of two pointed arches. Each has a span of 8 ft 6 in (2.6m) and carried a 12 ft (3.7m) wide roadway. There is a central pier 4 ft 6 in (1.4m) wide with triangular cutwaters on both the upstream and downstream faces; this is an unusual feature in Bedfordshire, as other medieval bridges in the county had cutwaters only on the upstream face.

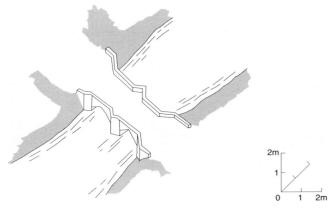

Fig 99 Arlesey bridge: reconstruction of medieval bridge

Fig 100 Arlesey bridge: south face

Datestones of 1683 on the downstream face and 1711 on the upstream face refer to repairs. Every stone voussoir in both arch rings has been refaced in brick, and the cutwaters heavily patched in both stone and brick.

When the bridge first appears in the Quarter Sessions records in 1807 it is described as being badly in need of repair.[7] The subsequent work included the 'Use of Pils [piles] and Planks and Bords for Stankin [damming] to Turn the Water to Repair the Bottom of the Bridge – £1 10s 0d', carriage of stone from 'Rowni pit [in Southill] – £1 2s 0d'[8] and '5 Yards of Stone for Rocking the Foundation of the Bridge – 7s 6d'.[9]

PHASE 2 – 1851

By 1851, the timber railings were in a decayed state, and the bridge was considered too narrow for the increased traffic generated by the Great Northern Railway and the adjacent station which had just been opened. A single span brick arch was therefore built against the downstream face, increasing the overall width to 14 ft 6 in (4.4m).[10] An inscribed keystone records the work.

PHASE 3 – LATE 19th-20th CENTURY

There were three subsequent widenings of the bridge. The precise sequence is unclear, although the first upstream widening is probably the earliest. It increased the overall width to 18 ft 8 in (5.7m) and was achieved by laying a massive iron girder across the top of the upstream cutwater. New concrete supports were added, obscuring what remained of the medieval abutments. Two further widenings, one to each face of the bridge, also rested on concrete abutments and carried footpaths nearly 6 ft (1.8m) wide. The downstream widening was completed first with the upstream widening following in 1937,[11] but these have since been removed.

NOTES
1 TL 189 378; HER 5208; see also Peter McKeague, 'Two little-known Bedfordshire Bridges', *Beds Mag* 21 no 167, Winter 1988, 281-284

2   Beds RO: IN 58, 1378/79 no 3 (Court Rolls and Registers of the Manor of Arlesey Bury, transcribed in CRT 130 ARL 9)
3   Beds RO: IN 58, 1396-97 no 8
4   Beds RO: IN 62, 1498/99 no 2
5   Beds RO: IN 61, 1466/67 no 5
6   Beds RO: CRT 130 ARL 2, transcription of 'Survey of Etonsbury Manor 1566' in uncatalogued bundle 13
7   Beds RO: QBM 1, 47-49; QSR 20, 1807, 138-139
8   Beds RO: QSR 1808, 106
9   Beds RO: QSR 1808, 109
10   Beds RO: QBM 1, 341
11   In *Beds Mag* 21, *op cit,* 283 the downstream widening is given as later. This is not so

CLAY BRIDGE, Clifton

THE EARLY BRIDGE

Clay bridge crossed the River Ivel north-west of Clifton.[1] There are no known medieval references, but the existence of a medieval bridge is suggested by the will of John Foster who in 1527 left 'to repairing Clee bridge ... a ewe sheep'.[2]

It was repaired by the County in 1807,[3] but destroyed in the great flood of 1st November 1823. It had comprised two brick arches, each 13 ft (4m) wide,[4] and the ruins were sketched by R Carter Smith (Fig 101).[5] It is unlikely to have been very old when washed away: the earliest surviving brick bridge in Bedfordshire is Smeaton's bridge at Cardington built in 1778 (see above), and brick was not widely used as a building material until the 16th and 17th centuries.[6]

The bridge destroyed in 1823 is therefore likely to have been a post-medieval replacement of an earlier, possibly medieval bridge; or perhaps the brickwork was a later refacing of a badly eroded sandstone structure.

THE 19th CENTURY IRON BRIDGE

The new bridge of 1824 was of iron, and had a single arch with a 28 ft (8.5m) span; this was designed to give 'greater water space without the impediment of an actual pier'.[7] The ironwork was made by Lees Cottam and Hallem of Coalbrookdale, and as other early iron bridges ordered by the County, was transported down the canal network to Linford wharf near Newport Pagnell and thence overland.[8] An inspection of the bridge in 1873, following the collapse of Broom bridge beneath the weight of a traction engine, noted that the iron girders were cast in two pieces and joined in the centre, causing vibrations when carts passed over. The centre girder had

Fig 101 Clay bridge, Clifton: after floods in 1823 (Beds Record Office: X 254/88/93)

Fig 102 Clay bridge, Clifton: iron bridge before demolition, c.1968 (Co Engineer)

been repaired and the bridge could only support a 7 ton (7.1 tonnes) weight. The report recommended inserting six new iron trellis girders to reinforce the outer part of the old girders and the iron plates that support the road; the cost would be £135.[9]

This bridge was photographed shortly before its demolition in 1968/69 (Fig 102). The braced iron girders show large triangular cut-outs in their spandrels. The joint referred to in the 1873 survey is visible at the centre of the arch, and the trellis girders inserted in 1873 may be seen through the open spandrels of the outermost girder. The upper surface of the girders is flat, supporting ornamental iron rails and a level roadway. The whole bridge rests on brick-faced abutments whose walls extend some way either side of the crossing as revetments for the river bank.

NOTES
1 TL 163 398; HER 1987
2 Beds RO: ABP/R 2 no 54 f52
3 Beds RO: QBM 1, 47-49
4 Beds RO: QBM 1, 152 (1824)
5 Beds RO: X 254/88/93
6 A Cox, *Brickmaking: A history and gazetteer,* Survey of Bedfordshire, 1979, 13
7 Beds RO: QBM 1, 144, 152
8 Beds RO: QSR 27, 1825, 450
9 Beds RO: QBC 5

SHEFFORD BRIDGES

Shefford lies at the confluence of the River Flit and its southern tributary, the Hit. Both rivers are crossed by the Bedford to Hitchin road, but no mention of bridges is found before 1560. In that year Robert Lucas of Shefford granted all his messuages, lands, meadows and hereditaments, 'to and for the yearly repairing, and maintaining

and keeping of the bridges, causeys and highways within the said town of Sherford in good and sufficient repair'; this either established a new charitable trust or enriched an existing one.[1]

The town of Shefford maintained its own bridges, in accordance with Henry VIII's 1530/31 statute which made boroughs responsible for all the bridges within their boundaries;[2] after 1560 the duties were carried out through the town charity.

Little is known of the early bridges of the town, as both the North bridge over the Flit[3] and the South bridge[4] over the Hit were replaced in the 19th and again in the 20th centuries. A brief record survives from 1803, when the Quarter Sessions noted that the North bridge consisted of four water piers; this suggests a five-arched bridge which must have been either brick or stone built.[5] It would have been quite a substantial structure over the relatively narrow river.

THE 19th CENTURY BRIDGES

In 1828 the Shefford Charity estate argued that the County ought to maintain the town's bridges.[6] Following some discussion, both North and South bridge were replaced at the County's expense by iron bridges costing £1100.[7] The documentation is sketchy but the ironwork for the South bridge, at least, was manufactured in the town by Walker and Yeats.[8]

Detailed surveys were carried out on both bridges in 1873, following the collapse of Broom bridge.[9] The North bridge had a 21 ft 6 in (6.6m) span supporting a 22 ft (6.7m) wide carriageway between the parapet railings. It had nine iron girders resting on iron templates placed on brick piers. The girders were set 2 ft 5 in (0.7m) apart with flanges on each side to carry the iron plates on which the gravel roadway was laid. These plates were 7/8 in (22mm) thick with slight ribs across them. (These dimensions are very close to those of the Lock Bridge, Broom, discussed below.) Each girder could carry a stationary load of 3 tons in the middle of its length. All nine could carry 27 tons (27.4 tonnes), or 54 tons (54.9 tonnes) if the weight was distributed over the whole length. The South bridge was similar, though with only a 16 ft 2 in (4.9m) span.

The South bridge was replaced in 1935 and the North in 1970.[10] Few illustrations of the old bridges survive, though plans for strengthening the North bridge in 1873 have been preserved (Fig 103).[11] The original girders were similar to those at Clay bridge. They were flat on top, but with curved braces beneath and large triangular cutouts in the 'spandrels'. The iron railings incorporated decorative latticework. The South bridge is likely to have been of similar appearance but no illustrations are available.

NOTES
1 Beds RO: QBP 7, 1803 – Transcript of earliest surviving document of the Town Charity containing historical background

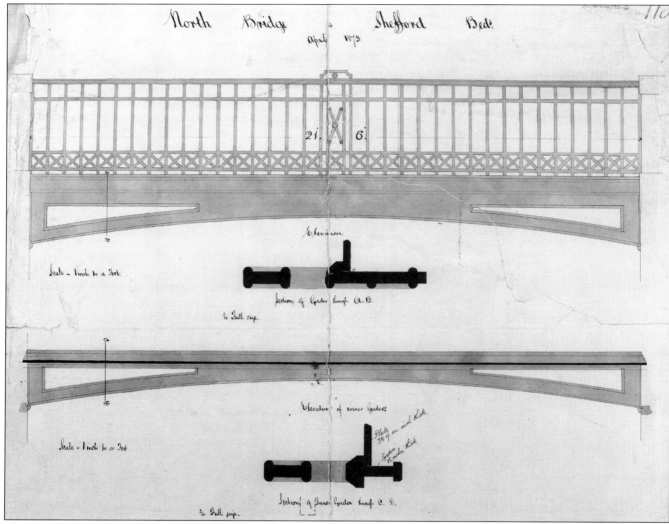

Fig 103 Shefford North bridge: 1873 survey drawings

2   22 Henry VIII, c5
3   TL 143 393; HER 15745
4   TL 145 390; HER 15746
5   Beds RO: QSR 19, 1803, 111
6   Beds RO: QBM 1, 209
7   Beds RO: QBM 1, 224 (1828)
8   Beds RO: QBM 1, 225 (1828)
9   Beds RO: QBC 5
10 *Lockgate* I no 6, Jan 1963, 91-96
11 Drawings in HER: BR/A600/45 – 6, 7

the cascade or weir. The landscaping is probably of 18th century date – the cascade is referred to in the Osborn accounts for 1756[2] – and the bridge may have been built at the same time or soon afterwards.

Architecturally the bridge is very similar to the dilapidated structure further upstream at Clophill (see below), and may be a close contemporary or even built by the same masons. Both are in local sandstone with three low

CHICKSANDS BRIDGE

Nothing is known about the history of this bridge,[1] which lies within the grounds of Chicksands Priory, a former Gilbertine Priory and later home of the Osborn family. It is shown on Jefferys' County Map of 1765, carrying the road from Campton to Haynes over the Flit. The River Flit has been artificially widened to the west of the bridge within the grounds of the Priory, and to the east as far as

Fig 104 Chicksands bridge: west face

elliptical arches. At Chicksands stepped half-pyramid cutwaters survive on both faces. Chicksands bridge is, however, much more substantial than Clophill, spanning the full breadth of the artificial channel. The present red brick parapets are modern, replacing a post and chain fence visible in a photograph of 1927.[3] The elevations are now somewhat obscured by the attachment of large metal pipes against each face. The bridge carries pedestrian traffic only and the deck has been resurfaced in red brick.

NOTES
1 TL 125 392; HER 15692
2 Beds RO: O 149
3 Beds RO: X 498/5

BEADLOW BRIDGES

At Beadlow, east of Clophill, the River Flit runs in three channels, each of which is bridged by the old Clophill-Shefford road.[1] The main bridge is that over the central channel, and is probably the 'Beadlow bridge' referred to in County records from 1795.[2] At that date Rev Edward Hervey of Aspley Guise was indicted at the Quarter Sessions for failing to repair it. As the nephew of Sir Boteler Chernock, formerly lord of the manor of Beadlow and heir to the Priory there, the Sessions considered him liable for the bridge. However the case was not successful and the bridge became a County bridge soon after. A 'second or small arch' was added after the enclosure of the parish in 1808[3] and an arch was reconstructed in 1824.[4]

Of the present bridges, the most northerly has been rebuilt entirely in blue engineering brick and widened on the downstream side by an iron girder placed out over the wing walls. The main channel is spanned by a two-arch brick bridge; it retains some sandstone in the lower courses of each arch. There is a cutwater on the upstream

Fig 105 Beadlow bridges: arches over main channel, west face

(west) face, in the shape of an elongated slightly rounded half pyramid tapering gently to an apex level with the arch crowns (Fig 105). Its form indicates a late post-medieval date, probably 19th century. The third bridge is no more than a low culvert, but it retains much sandstone in the lower courses.

NOTES
1 TL 105 383; HER 15693
2 Beds RO: QBM 1, 32
3 Beds RO: QBP 2 – report by Theed Pearse, 9.6.1854
4 Beds RO: QSR 26, 1824, 532; QBM 1, 156-157 (1825)

CLOPHILL BRIDGE

Clophill bridge, on the south side of the village green, formerly carried the main road north from St Albans and Luton towards Bedford over the River Flit.[1] Little is known about its early history, though 'Treubruge Croft', mentioned in a 12th century charter, has been said to refer to its original name of 'Tree bridge'.[2] A bridge at Clophill was mentioned in the will of John Samwell of Maulden in 1524.[3] In 1655, Sir John Charnock sold the Manor of Beadlow to Robert Bruce, together with the inn 'at the Sign of the Talbot' standing in 3 acres of ground 'over against' Clophill bridge.[4] It was shown on Ogilby's route map of 1675 as 'a stone bridg of four arches'.[5]

Fig 106 Clophill bridge: west face

The present bridge, now in a very dilapidated state, is of local sandstone. It has a central low elliptical arch about 11 ft 2 in (3.4m) wide and two small segmental outer arches, separated by half pyramid cutwaters on the upstream elevation. There were formerly cutwaters on the opposing face but these are now unidentifiable. From its style the bridge was probably built in the 18th century. It is very similar to Chicksands bridge (see above), and they are likely to be close in date or maybe even built by the same masons.

Clophill bridge was maintained by the County by 1824.[6] At some stage brick parapets were added but these have now given way to tubular railings. Another arch which lay to the south over a subsidiary channel has been replaced by a modern culvert with sandstone parapets. The main bridge was by-passed in 1937-38 and closed to traffic in 1957.

NOTES
1 TL 082 376; HER 10532
2 *Beds Mag* 8 no 62, Autumn 1962, 245-246
3 Beds RO: CRT 130 MAU 4D
4 *Beds Mag* 6, 1957/59, 289
5 M F Hopkinson, *Old county maps of Bedfordshire*, 1976, 9; Beds RO: Z 236/1
6 Beds RO: QBM 1, 142

HOLLINGTON BRIDGE

Hollington bridge lies on the road from Maulden to Flitton and Silsoe over the River Flit.[1] In a grant of c.1236 Godfrey de Linholt conceded to the canons of Dunstable Priory the right of 'building and repairing the causeway which is between Maulden and the barley mill ... which will have sufficient width [later given as 5 ft] for leading a horse laden with corn ... as far as the greater bridge'.[2]

A stream between 'Holyndon' bridge and 'Symmys' bridge is mentioned in the court rolls for 1519.[3] Land near 'Holyngden' bridge was also mentioned in the will of John Samwell of Maulden in 1524.[4] A new bridge was built in 1810;[5] this was evidently in brick as instructions were issued in 1858 to replace washed away brickwork with Silsoe stone (sandstone).[6] The bridge was described as of brick and sandstone in 1864.[7]

The area has now been considerably altered by the construction of the Ampthill bypass and no traces of the early crossings survive.

NOTES
1 TL 065 367; HER 15722
2 *BHRS* 10, 1926, 155 no 493
3 Beds RO: CRT 130 MAU 4C
4 Beds RO: CRT 130 MAU 4D
5 Beds RO: QSR, 1810, 33
6 Beds RO: QBM 1, 398
7 Beds RO: QBP 3

FLITWICK BRIDGE

The River Flit at East End, Flitwick divides into three separate courses, each bridged by an arch on the road to Greenfield and Westoning. The oldest arch appears to be the plain brick mill arch to the north; it is probably the bridge shown on Jefferys' county map of 1765. At the south end the single arch has been rebuilt, but the central channel is spanned by a rather fine arch in pale brown brick.[1] Its main interest lies in the detail of the parapets, which have recessed panels decorated by diaperwork

Fig 107 Flitwick bridge: north parapet

executed in blue brick, either side of a central pillar. The parapets end in large square terminals, and the whole is capped in blue brick of quite elaborate design. There is a course of bricks set in a 'cog' pattern immediately above the recessed panels and below the copings. A datestone records 'BEDS C C 1895', although the visible part of the bridge has been rebuilt in recent years, re-using the date stone, copings and pillar caps. Together with Tannery bridge, Potton, it was among the earliest bridges built by the modern County Council.[2]

NOTES
1 TL 043 347; HER 15701
2 Beds RO: Hi C M 2, p330

SOME OTHER BRIDGES OF THE IVEL AND FLIT VALLEYS

EARLY RECORDS

A claim for the oldest bridge in Bedfordshire – supposedly Roman – does not stand up to close examination. In 1962, a length of stone walling was found in the side of a drainage channel, in association with Roman material at **Ruxox** between Maulden and Flitwick.[1] However, the watercourse which cut through the structure was an artificial channel which was made on the enclosure of Maulden parish in 1797[2] and did not exist in Roman times. The wall almost certainly belonged to a Roman building.

Medieval references to bridges come from a variety of sources. **Wattle bridge** in Gravenhurst, on the upper reaches of the River Hit, is given a passing mention in the lease of a mill 'near the bridge of Watewale' by Ralph de Tyville to the abbot of Ramsey in 1265.[3] Stock bridge, in Newtown road, Henlow, on a small Ivel tributary, is recorded in the field name 'Stokebruggefurlong' in the early 15th century.[4] In 1499, the will of John Gray of Northill leaves 'to the repair of **Pekysbrech** 18d'.[5]

The location of **Sandy bridge** is uncertain. In 1504, Ralph Brunsale of Beeston left 3s 4d in his will to Sandy bridge;[6] this is definitely a different bridge from Girtford, which is also mentioned in the same will. Bailiffs' accounts for 1536/37 refer to '1 parcel meadow lying at Sandy bridge'.[7] It may have been situated at Sandy mill, where a bridge is shown in 1748 carrying the road from Sandy to Beeston over the River Ivel.[8]

The dangers which early bridges presented are highlighted by an entry in Campton parish register, recording the burial on 29th May 1599 of 'Elsabeth and Anne Ravens, which children weare drowned at **Mr Blofeld's bridge** followinge their mother to Meppersall'.[9] This bridge crossed the River Hit, possibly on the line of an old route from Campton to Meppershall which runs to the south-west of Woodhall Farm.[10]

POST-MEDIEVAL

As well as Wattle bridge (see above), other bridges in Gravenhurst are documented in the extensive Lucas collection in the Bedfordshire Record Office, demonstrating how the survival of early references to bridges depends very much on the survival of historic documentation for an area as a whole. **Mead Close bridge**,[11] **Hogsbridge**[12] field and **Handscombe bridge**[13] furlong are all mentioned in a document of 1638/39.[14] They lie on the upper reaches of the River Hit. Handscombe bridge is also known as **Ion bridge** in 1706/7, named after the hamlet nearby.[15] In 1813, it was considered repairable by Baroness Lucas of Wrest Park.[16]

Other bridges were repaired by their respective parishes. In **Harlington**, 13s 9d was spent on timber and 5s 8d for 'worke about the bridge' in 1678.[17] In 1679, the inhabitants of Southill were identified as responsible for the repair of **Holme Mills bridge,** south-west of Biggleswade.[18] However, the lord of the manor in Old Warden was liable for the repair of some bridges there. In 1689 the manor court roll recorded: 'Item we present ye lord of this Mannor for not repayring the **bridge next to Ox pytle** and also the **bridge next Ushras** ...'.[19]

Private individuals took responsibility for building

bridges as late as the 18th century. In 1796, a new arch was made by William Flint in **Meppershall**[20] over the town ditch at the junction of Hoo Lane and Chapel Road.

Finally, a small bridge on the road between Blunham and Tempsford, about 500m north-east of the river and navigation bridges, demonstrates how the remains of early structures can still be preserved within apparently modern bridges. **Brickgate bridge** spans what is now a backwater, though as the channel marks the ancient parish boundary it was probably once the main course of the River Ivel (Fig 79). Although the bridge has been rebuilt and widened in brick to the south, the footings of an earlier stone structure survive. It may be contemporary with the main river bridge to the west; it had certainly been there for some time before the Tempsford enclosure of 1778, when the road was re-aligned to the south and the brick widening became necessary.[21]

NOTES

1. *Luton News,* 7 September 1962; HER 918
2. Beds RO: MA 32
3. TL 119 357; HER 15702; *VCH* 2, 1908, 297
4. TL 174 390; HER 8397; *BHRS* 13, 1930, 164 no 214
5. HER 15727; *BHRS* 45, 1966, 10-11 no 24
6. *BHRS* 45, 1966, 41-42 no 91
7. *BHRS* 63, 1984, 98 no 129
8. Beds RO: HA 1334
9. *Beds Parish Registers* vol 52, 'Campton-with-Shefford'; V H Chambers, *Old Meppershall: a parish history,* 1979, 57
10. ?TL 131 377; HER 15725
11. Location unknown; HER 15764
12. TL 108 347; HER 15703
13. TL 110 338; HER 15704
14. Beds RO: L 6/63
15. Beds RO: L 6/51-2, deed
16. Beds RO: QBM 1, 62
17. TL 025 305; HER 15705; *Harlington parish survey,* unpub copy in Heritage Group, County Hall (primary source not recorded)
18. TL 184 428; HER 15688; Beds RO: HSA 1682 W7
19. HER 14117; W 2591 no 173, 1689
20. TL 141 366; HER 15723; Chambers, *op cit,* 56
21. TL 159 521; HER 15114; Beds RO: Enclosure Book D. Compare the road line shown on Jefferys' 1765 map of Bedfordshire, with that on a Tempsford map of c.1829 (Beds RO: X 1/41)

THE OUZEL VALLEY

The River Ouzel rises at the foot of Dunstable Downs, and flows northwards to join the Great Ouse at Newport Pagnell. Only a short stretch runs through Bedfordshire; before Linslade was transferred from Buckinghamshire in 1965, the Ouzel formed the county boundary.

A number of medieval crossings are suggested by a royal writ of 1347, ordering the sheriff of Buckinghamshire 'to cause as many bridges to be made from Leighton to Fenny Stratford as used to be there, and to compel all those who were bound to construct or repair those bridges so to do'[1]. Individual bridges are documented at Leighton Buzzard and Old Linslade (near Grange Mill) on the Bedfordshire county boundary, and at Fenny Stratford (on Watling Street) and Newport Pagnell in Buckinghamshire. There may have been others further south, on the sites of Slapton and Northall bridges in Billington parish.[2]

Clipstone Brook flows into the Ouzel south of Leighton Buzzard and was crossed by a bridge in Lake Street, documented in the late 15th century.

The bridges of the Grand Union Canal are discussed in a separate section (see below).

NOTES
1. *Cal of Close Rolls* 1346-9, 397, quoted in *Lockgate* II no 10, Jan 1968, 149
2. See Peter McKeague & Martin Cook, 'South Bedfordshire Bridges', *Beds Mag* 22 no 176, Spring 1991, 333-335

GRANGE or LINSLADE BRIDGE
Heath and Reach

In 1398, the court rolls of the manor of Leighton Buzzard record a 'presentment of want of repair of the moiety [half] of Grangebridge by default of the Abbot of Woburn'.[1] Woburn Abbey's only documented property in Leighton was Grange mill, west of Heath and Reach, and some surrounding land. The bridge may have connected this to other lands held in Linslade parish, then in Buckinghamshire. The bridge is likely to have been over the main course of the River Ouzel as this formed the county boundary;[2] the other 'moiety' (half) was probably the responsibility of an equivalent landowner in Buckinghamshire.

The bailiff's accounts of Leighton Buzzard manor for 1534/35 refer to Grange Mill bridge, alias Linslade bridge.[3] The name recalls the original site of Linslade, which was on the opposite side of the River Ouzel from Grange Mill; the modern town west of Leighton Buzzard developed in the 19th century as a result of the trade generated by the Grand Junction Canal and the railway.

NOTES
1. Beds RO: KK 944/1, Court roll extract
2. SP 909 271; HER 15057
3. J N Dalton (ed), *The Manuscripts of St George's Chapel, Windsor Castle,* 1957, 129, XV.61.71

LEIGHTON BRIDGE

Leighton bridge is first mentioned in 1311/12,[1] but there must already have been an important crossing here associated with the development of the town,[2] and the growth of Leighton in the 12th and 13th centuries saw a number of earlier routes converging on the bridge site. Even the important Saxon east-west route (Theedway), which crossed the Ouzel further south at 'Yttingaford' (first recorded in AD 906),[3] was drawn towards the river crossing at Leighton along what is now Stanbridge Road.[4]

Leighton bridge is named as 'Loventbrigge' bridge in the bailiff's accounts for 1389/90[5] and as 'Lovend brygge' bridge in 1489/90.[6] It was evidently the duty of the Manor of Leighton to maintain it. Further references are found in the manor court rolls (1555-58),[7] and in the accounts for 1611[8] and 1612,[9] the latter dealing with repairs. By the early 18th century, responsibility had passed to the Town, probably because the Dean and Chapter of Windsor, the Lords of the Manor of Leighton, lost their lands (and therefore responsibility for the bridge) during the Commonwealth period, 1649-1660.[10] In 1734 the Quarter Sessions approved a rate of 3d in the pound for the Leighton Highway Surveyor to repair the roads and rebuild the bridge.[11] It was again rebuilt by the Town in 1824, after severe flood damage.[12]

Proposals to widen the bridge in 1872 included a plan showing that it had two arches divided by a central pier with a cutwater.[13] The present bridge is a modern concrete structure.

NOTES
1. *Cal Inq Post Mortem* vol V, Edward II, 199
2. SP 917 250; HER 11094
3. *BHRS* 5, 1920, 163-180
4. S R Coleman, pers comm
5. The Aerary, St George's Chapel, Windsor Castle, XV 61 32
6. The Aerary, St George's Chapel, Windsor Castle, XV 61 53
7. Beds RO: KK 944/6
8. Beds RO: KK 769
9. Beds RO: KK 728 & 730
10. S R Coleman, *Leighton Buzzard Parish Survey*, 1981 unpub, 63 (copy in Heritage Group, County Hall)
11. Beds RO: QBM 1, 6
12. Beds RO: CRT 130 LEI 5b, Leighton Buzzard Vestry Minutes
13. Beds RO: QBP 3

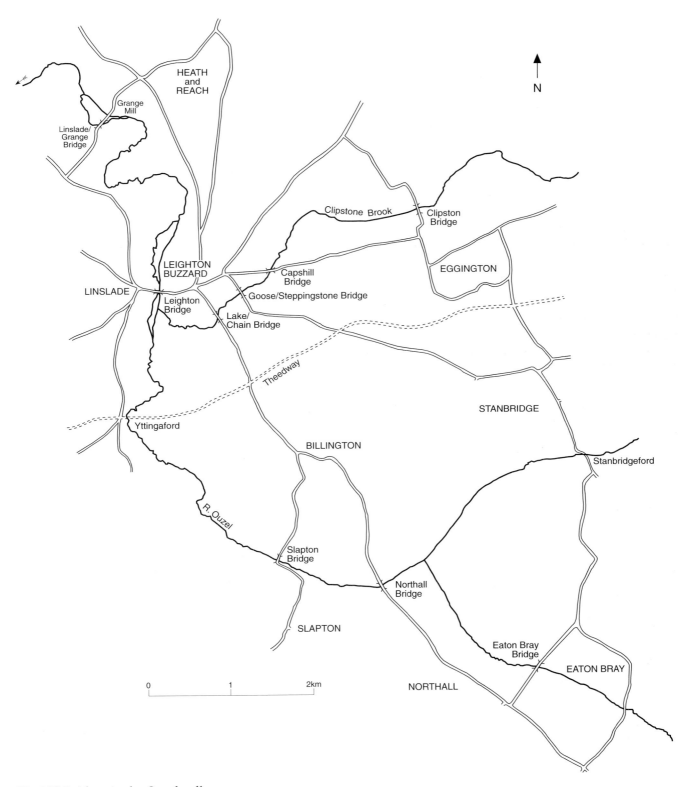

Fig 108 Bridges in the Ouzel valley

EATON BRAY BRIDGE

The bridge on the Northall road in Eaton Bray was built in 1898;[1] it is of historical rather than architectural interest, as it was one of the last bridges to be built locally and then transferred to the County under the terms of Lord Ellenborough's Act of Parliament of 1803 (see Historical Summary). The County Surveyor reported to the Highways and Bridges Committee: 'Eaton Bray Rural District Council requested me to watch the erection [of the new bridge] ... I have made several visits ... and have been satisfied each time, that from the foundation and upwards throughout, the work is sound and good and sufficient for all road traffic.'[2] As the bridge lies on the boundary with Buckinghamshire, the cost was probably shared with the adjacent parish of Edlesborough.

Fig 109 Eaton Bray bridge: south-east face

The bridge is of yellow-brown gault brick with two arches. The upstream face (Fig 109) has a very low cut-water protecting the pier base but the downstream face is plain. The parapets have square brick terminals and are devoid of detail except for commemorative stones recording the county boundary and the date of construction.

NOTES
1   SP 975 200; HER 15697
2   Beds RO: Hi C M 3, p226

SOME OTHER OUZEL VALLEY BRIDGES

AN EARLY BRIDGE PLACE-NAME?

It has been suggested that the name 'Stanbridge' (a village to the south-east of Leighton Buzzard) is derived from a stone bridge over the River Ouzel.[1] The earliest occurrence of the name refers to the Half-Hundred of Stanbridge in the Domesday Book of 1086. However, the existence of a Saxon or early Norman stone bridge would be surprising, given the absence of suitable building material in the area. Otherwise, the earliest documented bridge in the parish is at **Stanbridgeford,** built in 1814.[2]

MEDIEVAL

Apart from Leighton and Linslade (Grange) bridges, the presence of other bridges over the River Ouzel in medieval times can be inferred from later records. Slapton bridge on the Billington-Slapton road first appears in bailiff's accounts for 1415/16;[3] it had probably already been there for some time. It is on the county boundary (Slapton is in Buckinghamshire) and was jointly repaired by Bedfordshire and Buckinghamshire in 1839.[4]

Northall bridge, also in Billington, is not recorded until the 18th century (it appears on Jefferys' map of 1765 as 'Northill bridge').[5] In 1822 the Quarter Sessions noted that it was formerly expected to have been repaired at the expense of the lords of the manor of Billington in Leighton Buzzard and Northall in Buckinghamshire.[6] This evidence for a long period of maintenance suggests that the bridge may have had a medieval predecessor. The County did however accept liability in 1839, when the bridge was jointly repaired with Buckinghamshire at the same time as Slapton.[7]

Over the Clipstone Brook in Leighton Buzzard, **Lake** or **Chain bridge** was mentioned in the manor court rolls for 1491.[8] In 1802, the Vestry Minutes record a 'request that Benjamin Bevan ... make a Plan & Estimate for Erection of a new Bridge over the River at the Lake End of Town (in lieu of the old one considered to be past repair) ... that an application be made ... for allowance out of the Co Rate'.[9]

Braiton bridge in Aspley Guise, on a small tributary of the Ouzel, was mentioned in the manor court rolls for 1592 as 'Brayden bridge'. Its repair seems later to have become part of rental arrangement: the roll for 1668 records '... that Jas Ambridge shall maintain and keep Draighton Bridge in sufficient repair in lieu of one rood of meadow in Broad Mead belonging to our Town'.[10]

POST-MEDIEVAL

The growth of traffic along Watling Street (now the A5) and the Woburn turnpike road, led to the provision of several bridges across the upper reaches of Clipstone Brook and its tributaries. A new 3-arched brick bridge was built at **Hockliffe** in 1772, on the Woburn Turnpike just beyond the point where it branches off Watling Street. It was dilapidated by 1824, and the road was re-aligned in order to avoid the sharp bend that the bridge had created.[11] Remains of the brick abutments are still visible beneath a modern footbridge. Also on Clipstone Brook, a bridge called **Goose bridge,** in South Street, Leighton Buzzard was demolished in 1845 and its material used to build **Steppingstone bridge** on the same site.[12] **Capshill bridge** was recorded in 1739[13] and rebuilt in 1803.[14] **Clipston bridge** in Eggington parish was built in 1868.[15]

Lord Ellenborough's Act of 1803 enabled the County to take over any new bridges provided they were judged suitable, and the parish of Salford soon took advantage of the new arrangements. In 1821, John Morris, the **Salford** parish surveyor, requested an inspection of the new bridge at **Low Bush** on the Salford-Broughton road so that the bridge might thereafter be repaired at the expense of the County.[16]

NOTES
1   Mawer & Stenton, 1926, 132
2   SP 970 230; HER 15756; QBP 1, 1849
3   SP 932 216; HER 15690; J N Dalton (ed), *The Manuscripts of St George's Chapel, Windsor Castle,* 1957, 129, XV.61.34
4   Beds RO: QBM 1, 291
5   SP 945 213; HER 15691
6   Beds RO: QSR 25, 1822, 412
7   Beds RO: QBM 1, 291 (where it is named 'Billington bridge')
8   SP 924 247; HER 11087; Beds RO: KK 944/4
9   Beds RO: CRT 130 LEI 5b
10   SP 936 372; HER 10109; Beds RO: HO 63
11   SP 974 270; HER 9954; Minutes of the Turnpike Trustees for 1772 and 1824, transcribed in A W Parker, *The Woburn Toll road 1728-1860,* 1975
12   SP 927 250; HER 11064; Beds RO: BO 1623
13   SP 931 253; HER 11069; Beds RO: NC 269
14   Beds RO: QSR 19, 1803, 5
15   SP 948 261; HER 15699; Beds RO: QBC 4
16   SP 925 395; HER 15740; Beds RO: QSR 1821, 540; QBM 1, 128-129

THE LEA VALLEY

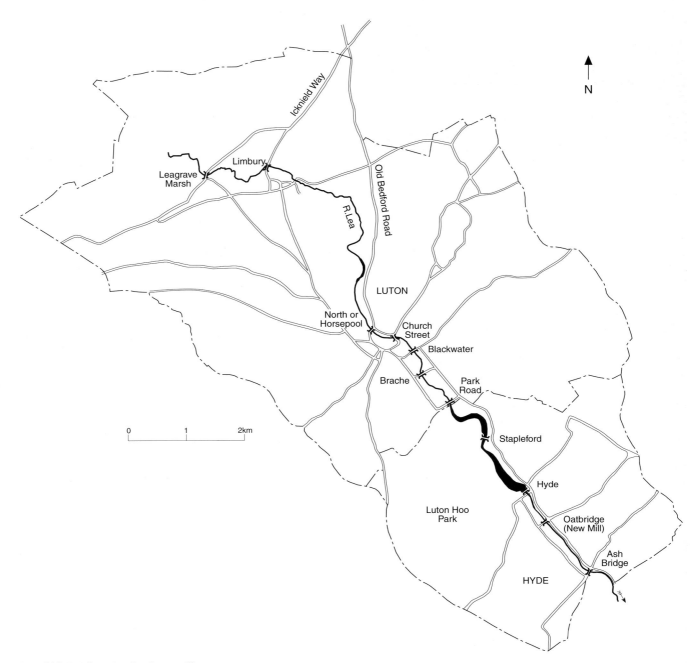

Fig 110 Bridges in the Lea valley

The River Lea rises in Leagrave marsh and flows southwards through Luton and Hyde into Hertfordshire, eventually joining the River Thames. The major medieval highway in the area was that which ran from Bedford through Luton to St Albans. Other roads ran east to Hitchin and west to Dunstable.

Although the Lea is not a large river, it was bridged at several points in the medieval period. William Austin, in his History of Luton (1928), listed eight bridges which existed in Luton parish (including Hyde) in the mid-18th century.[1]

NOTES

1 W Austin, *The history of Luton and its hamlets,* 1928, vol 2, appendix I, 340; see also Peter McKeague & Martin Cook, 'South Bedfordshire Bridges' *Beds Mag* 22 no 176, Spring 1991, 333-335

HYDE BRIDGE, Luton Hoo

The use of iron bridges became widespread during the early 19th century, and once their durability had been proven, the

Fig 111 Hyde bridge, Luton Hoo

technique began to be adopted by private landowners. As an example of this, the Marquis of Bute paid £475 for a single span iron bridge which was erected over the River Lea in the grounds of his Luton Hoo estate by 1831.[1] The bridge, with a 45 ft (13.7m) span and 14 ft (14.3m) carriageway, was cast by Barwell and Hagger of Northampton.[2]

It still stands in the grounds of Luton Hoo, and is almost double the span of any previously constructed iron bridge in the county. The girders appear to be cast in one piece, with open latticework infilling the spandrels. There is a moulded underside to the top edge of the girders which support decorative iron railings. The bridge rests on brick abutments with stone footings. These extend to parapet level forming stone piers, interrupting the iron railings which continue beyond on the long gently curving approaches.[3]

NOTES
1   TL 117 186; HER 6895
2   Beds RO: G/DDA 162

3   Dept of the Environment, *District of South Beds, 14th List of Buildings of Special Architectural and Historic Interest,* 26.9.1980

BRACHE BRIDGE

A bridge was apparently awaiting construction at Brache in 1551 when the manor court recorded that 'John Camfeild has taken away 6 planks 14 inches [355mm] wide and 10 foot [3.1m] long and 3 inches [76mm] in thickness, and 2 groundsills 12 feet [3.65m] long and 2 rafters, from the way leading from Luton to Brache, and a pain is imposed that he carries back the said objects to the same place where the bridge is to be made before the feast of St Michael'.[1] The bridge was evidently to be of wooden trestle construction little different from those medieval timber bridges identified by Rigold;[2] from the dimensions given it was only a minor structure, and easily stolen![3]

NOTES
1   Beds RO: CRV 25/92, manor court roll for 8.10.1551; W Austin, *The History of Luton and its Hamlets,* vol I, 1928, 246
2   S E Rigold, 'Structural Aspects of Medieval Bridges', *Medieval Archaeology* 19, 1975, 48-91
3   TL 099 206; HER 15714

HORSEPOOL or NORTH BRIDGE, Luton

Horsepool or North bridge in Bridge Street, Luton, was probably the most important of the Lea bridges, carrying

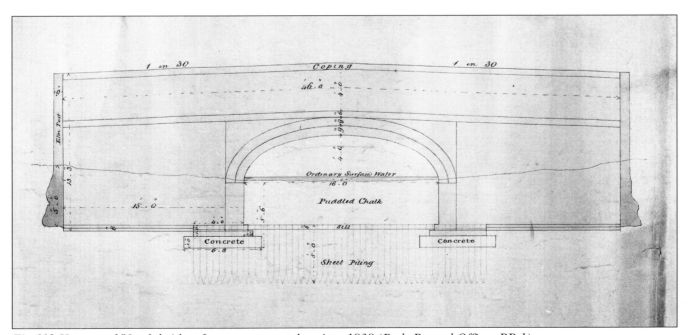

Fig 112 Horsepool/North bridge, Luton: contract drawing, 1838 (Beds Record Office: PB 1)

the main highway north from the town.[1] It is identified by Austin as the bridge referred to in a 1194-96 charter of Earl Baldwin de Betune, Earl of Albermarle.[2] It was mentioned in a will of 1526, when 13s 4d was left to 'the mending of the highway at Norrebrigg'.[3] Ogilby's route map of 1675 shows the St Albans to Bedford road crossing the Lea at this point but does not give a description of the bridge.[4]

By 1795 there was only a timber footbridge by a ford and all the carriages had to pass through 'horse-pool'.[5] This was replaced in 1797 by two brick bridges and the overall road level was built up 7 ft (2.1m).[6] There were evidently two channels here, one of which was the leat for the nearby mill.

In 1834 the Quarter Sessions proposed that the two bridges be replaced by a single structure but the Marquis of Bute, the landowner, objected.[7] Instead a scheme was proposed to erect a 12ft (3.7m) arch over the main stream and a separate 10ft (3.0m) arch over the mill stream.[8] Both bridges have since been replaced, but the detailed contract and drawings of 1838 survive, recording the nature of these unusual structures.[9]

Brickwork from the 1797 bridges was reused in the foundations and backing for the abutments. The foundations were to comprise 1 foot (305mm) of concrete on which the brickwork was to commence. On the sides of each abutment 2 inch (50mm) elm or beech piles, used green, were to be driven 5 ft (1.5m) below the foundations, with an elm or beech sill 5 in by 2 in (125mm by 50mm), again used green (Fig 112). The bridges above were to be brick-built, and to have brick parapets capped with semi-circular brick copings. The parapets terminated in elm posts.

The arch floors were to be formed of compacted well puddled chalk and gravel laid in courses 6 inches (150mm) thick, and to be well rammed and consolidated. The core of the bridge was to be infilled with sound soil, chalk or gravel, again in well-compacted 6 inch (150mm) thick courses, and the extrados of each arch was to be lined with 6 inches (150mm) of concrete. The bridges were to be covered in sound new bricks. The road between the bridges was to be embanked with an incline of 1 in 30 on the approaches. Even though the bridges no longer survive, the contract makes interesting reading and provides some insight into the construction techniques in use at the time. These bridges were destroyed by flood in 1879.[10]

NOTES
1   TL 090 215; HER 15715
2   *BHRS* 2, 1914, 157-184, 161; *BHRS* 3, 1916, 223
3   Beds RO: ABP/R 2 f30
4   M F Hopkinson, *Old County Maps of Bedfordshire,* 1976, 9; Beds RO: Z 236/1
5   W Austin, *The History of Luton and its Hamlets,* vol II, 1928, 94
6   *ibid,* 96; Beds RO: QBP 1, 1833
7   Beds RO: QBM 1, 256; QBP 1
8   Beds RO: QBM 1, 259 (1834)
9   Beds RO: QBP 1; PB 1
10 Beds RO: QBP 5

SOME OTHER LEA VALLEY BRIDGES

After Horsepool/North bridge, the earliest documented bridge over the River Lea in Bedfordshire is at Limbury north of Luton,[1] which featured in a dispute over profits from **Limbury** millpond in 1317.[2] Austin named it as **Tanyard bridge.**[3] **Stapleford bridge,** recorded in 1391/92,[4] crossed the Lea at a mill site which probably stood where the two lakes now meet in Luton Hoo Park.[5] **Oatbridge,** at Newmill End, Hyde[6] occurs in a 1486 deed describing land 'abutting on the way from Stapulford to Otebygge, and on the river Lygh'.[7] **Ash bridge**[8] on the East Hyde-Thrales End road, first appears as 'Ackewoode bridge' in 1565.[9]

Within Luton itself, the Lea crossing in **Church Street** consisted of 'a raised path, with a plank across the stream serving for foot passengers' until the late 18th century. A two-arched brick bridge was built in 1799.[10] **'Stopsley bridge'** referred to in 1596[11] may have been on the same site, which is on the road to Stopsley.

Of the other bridges which Austin mentioned as standing in the mid-18th century,[12] no earlier records have been identified. **Leagrave Marsh bridge** lay on the Bramingham Road near Leagrave Mill.[13] Austin placed **Stocking bridge**[14] in Stockingstone Lane, though this road did not actually cross the Lea until the New Bedford Road was built in 1806. **Park Road bridge**[15] and **Blackwater bridge** in Lea Road (now under the inner ring road)[16] complete his list of main bridges. He also mentioned a timber bridge at Little Moor near Guildford Street, and two in Barbers Lane; these were minor structures, and probably of no great age.

The Quarter Sessions bridge minutes record a bridge being dismantled by Lord Hampton of Luton at **Pepper Lane** (or Alley, otherwise known as Rosemary Lane or Louce Lane) leading to Little Moor in 1808.[17] Apparently ten carts of timber and ten more of ironwork were taken away from the site.

NOTES
1   TL 077 242; HER 15717
2   *BHRS* 3, 1916, 221-2
3   W Austin, *The history of Luton and its hamlets,* 1928, vol 2, App I, 340
4   Beds RO: DW 27
5   TL 109 197; HER 15708; *BHRS* 3, 1916, 233; 'Stapleford' is also named at this location on Gordon's 1736 map of Bedfordshire
6   TL 120 181; HER 15707
7   Beds RO: DW 287
8   TL 128 172; HER 15706
9   Beds RO: DW 74
10 TL 094 213; HER 15765; Austin, *op cit,* 96
11 Beds RO: DW 101
12 Austin, *op cit,* 340
13 TL 061 242; HER 15718
14 HER 15719
15 TL 104 202; HER 15768
16 TL 097 211; HER 15720
17 HER 15721; Beds RO: QSR 20, 1808, 157

THE IVEL NAVIGATION

In 1757, the Ivel Navigation Act gave approval for the canalising of the River Ivel from its confluence with the Great Ouse at Tempsford to Biggleswade, Shefford, Baldock and Hitchin. This was seen as a desirable and potentially profit-making scheme:

'... the making and completing such Navigation will be of great Benefit and Advantage, not only to the Inhabitants of the several populous Towns of Bigleswade [sic], Shefford, Hitchin and Baldock, but to the Inhabitants of the Country in general for many Miles round, by supplying them with Coals and other necessary Commodities, at a much cheaper Rate than they now pay for the same by Land Carriage ...'[1]

The first stage of the work extended as far south as Biggleswade in 1758. A series of new locks and staunches were built and a navigation channel was cut at Blunham to bypass the 17th century bridge and the watermill upstream. A new bridge was added over the cut but was replaced in later works. None of the existing bridges upstream of Blunham seems to have caused an obstruction for the boats. The replacement of Girtford and

Biggleswade bridges in the later 18th century reflects the increased traffic along the turnpikes, rather than problems for navigation.

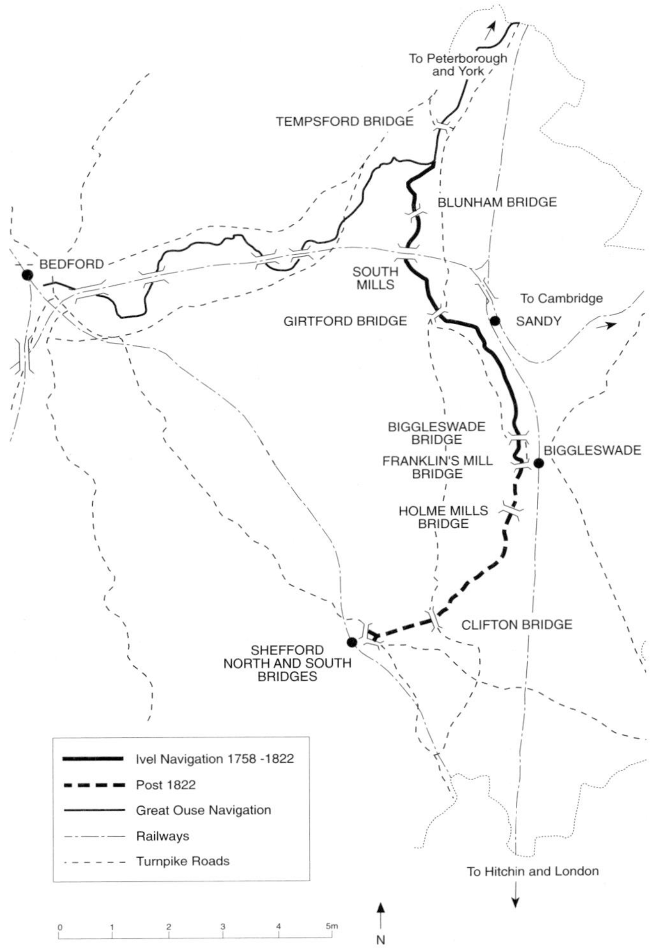

The opening of the Ivel Navigation was commemorated by an inscription on the old Biggleswade bridge:-

'The river Ivel, made navigable
from Tempsford
to Biggleswade
in the year of Our Lord . . . '
'1758'[2]

In 1822 work began on extending the navigable waterway to Shefford, and locks along the existing section were reconstructed. Upstream of Langford, a new channel was cut as far as Shefford. In 1823 the Navigation commissioners erected a series of cast iron girder bridges, at Blunham, Franklin's Mill (Biggleswade), Holme Mills and Clifton. The bridges were made by Moreton and Kinman of Biggleswade, following similar, though not identical, designs apparently drawn up by Francis Giles of Bristol, who also became the second County Surveyor in 1823.[3] They were the first iron bridges to be made locally rather than imported from Coalbrookdale. The few remaining structures are the earliest surviving iron bridges in the county.[4]

Unable to compete with the new railways, the Ivel Navigation was wound up in 1876 by the Ivel Navigation (Abandonment) Act.[5]

NOTES

1 30 Geo II, c42
2 Beds RO: CRT 130 Biggleswade 7 – Notes on Stones from Old Biggleswade Bridge
3 English Heritage Scheduled Ancient Monument Record form, Bedfordshire no 87
4 See also Martin Cook & Peter McKeague, 'The Ivel Navigation and its bridges', *Beds Mag* 22 no 175, Winter 1990, 289-294; *Lockgate* I no 3, Apr 1962, 30-34; I no 4, Jul 1962, 61-64; I no 5, Oct 1962, 80-83; I no 6, Jan 1963, 88-90
5 39/40 Vic, 1876

BLUNHAM NAVIGATION BRIDGE

The navigation channel at Blunham, which was cut during the first phase of the development of the Ivel Navigation in 1758, required the provision of a bridge on the Blunham-Tempsford road, close to the 17th century bridge over the original river. The character of this first bridge is unknown, but it is shown on Jefferys' County Map of 1765.

The present structure dates from the Navigation improvements of 1823 and is the most complete and unaltered of the standard Navigation bridges of the time.[1] The

Fig 113 Map of the Ivel Navigation
(Drawing by Martin Cook)

Fig 114 Blunham navigation bridge: from the south-east

Blunham navigation bridge retained its original railings until very recently; these were bolted to the upper surface of the outside girders, and had square terminals of open railings at each end. They were replaced by iron replicas when the bridge was repaired in 1992 (Fig 114). The approach roads were originally unfenced though tubular steel railings have now been erected.

NOTES
1   TL 155 519; HER 15057; see also Peter McKeague, 'Blunham Bridges' *Beds Mag* 21 no 168, Spring 1989, 333-336

span consists of a series of five curved cast iron beams resting on abutments constructed from massive blocks of sandstone. The beams, which are functionally plain, are held together by a pair of ties at right angles to the carriageway, and the deck is formed by iron plates resting on top of the girders. The maker's name plate ('Moreton and Kinman, Biggleswade') is bolted to the west abutment immediately below the south girder. A narrow ledge which forms a footpath below the bridge against the east abutment allowed boats to be guided through while the tow-horse went over the top of the roadway.

FRANKLIN'S MILL NAVIGATION BRIDGE, Biggleswade

A standard Ivel Navigation bridge was built at Franklin's Mill, Biggleswade, in 1823[1]. It was replaced in 1973, but several early 20th century photographs[2] show a typical Moreton and Kinman bridge with lattice-work iron railings and massively built sandstone wing walls (Fig 115).

NOTES
1   TL 187 444; HER 15686
2   Beds RO: eg X 425/17

Fig 115 Franklin's Mill, Biggleswade: mill and navigation bridge from the north-west, early 20th century
(Beds Record Office: X 425/17)

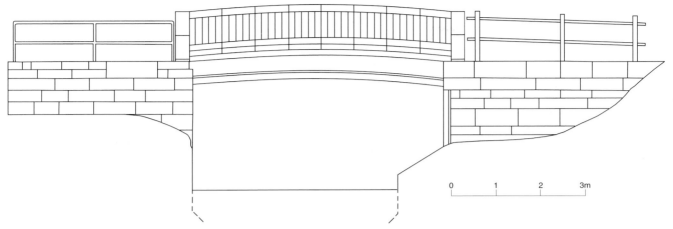

Fig 116 Blunham navigation bridge: drawing of south elevation

Fig 117 Lock bridge, Broom: south face, 1968, before removal of stone parapets (Beds Photographic Services)

96

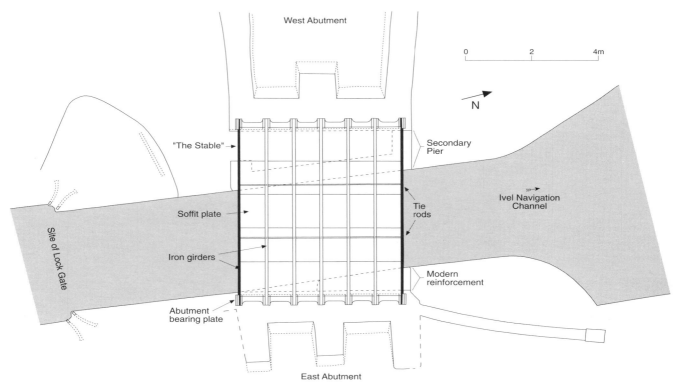

Fig 118 Lock bridge, Broom: plan of bridge structure

Fig 119 Lock bridge, Broom: excavated abutment and ironwork, from the west

LOCK BRIDGE, Broom

The navigation bridge near Holme Mills, south of Biggleswade, was built in 1823, together with the adjacent lock.[1] The superstructure of the bridge is not as well preserved as that at Blunham, but extensive repairs in 1993 allowed a very detailed record to be made. The abutments are built from massive blocks of locally quarried sandstone and the abutment walls extend southwards to form the side walls of the lock chamber (Figs 118 and 119). On the north side they open out from the lock to the full width of the navigation. The rear of each abutment is firmly secured into the bank by three substantial buttresses; the outer buttresses on the west side also served as wing walls. These details were exposed during excavation for reinforcement works.

Fig 120 Lock bridge, Broom: close-up of ironwork over east abutment

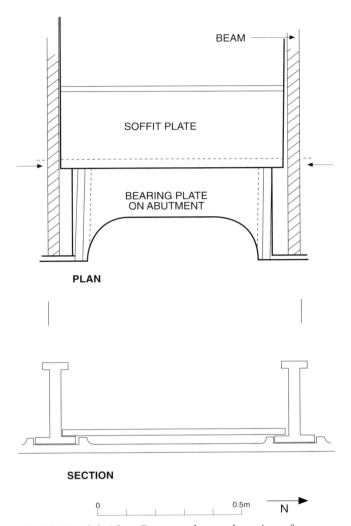

Fig 121 Lock bridge, Broom: plan and section of ironwork over east abutment

An iron template sits along the top of each abutment, secured in place by a longitudinal rib on its lower surface which fits into a slot cut into the top course of sandstone. On the upper face of the template integral sockets bear the ends of the seven iron girders. Between each girder, resting on the lower flange, is laid a series of five iron soffit plates, each strengthened on the upper side by two stiffening ribs perpendicular to the girders (Figs 120 and 121). The outer girders extend upwards to form retaining plates for the fill of the road deck. On their internal face, there are sockets for the original rails; the iron posts have been cut off, leaving the bases in place in the sockets. The upstream girder bears the date '1823' on its exposed surface and the whole structure is braced by two tie-rods. Stone parapets above the wing walls were in place until the late 1960s, but only that to the north-east still survives.

On the west abutment, a ledge originally carried a footpath beneath the bridge. This was blocked off at some time after the abandonment of the navigation, creating a narrow recess entered from the south, known locally as 'the stable'. The stonework butted against the underside of the iron girders, creating a 'see-saw' effect as traffic crossed the bridge, and giving rise to the structural problems which occasioned the recent repairs.

NOTES
1   TL 184 430; HER 3287

CLIFTON NAVIGATION BRIDGE

With the excavation of the Navigation channel between Langford and Shefford in 1823, a new bridge was needed on the Clifton-Stanford road, north of the ancient Clay bridge. The Navigation channel was filled in and the bridge demolished in 1968, but photographs taken at the time show it to have been of the standard Ivel Navigation bridge type made by Moreton and Kinman (Fig 122).[1] Surprisingly the decorative lattice work, identical to that

Fig 122 Clifton navigation bridge: before demolition in 1968 (Co Engineer)

on Franklin's Mill bridge, had survived until 1968, whilst the iron girders below had not. These had been replaced by straight girders and the void between them and the railings patched with brick. As at Lock bridge, Broom, the footpath beneath the bridge had been blocked off at some stage. There were massive sandstone wing walls.

NOTES
1   TL 162 398; HER 1988

KING'S BRIDGE, Southill

A small iron girder bridge lies hidden in woodland immediately east of the Old Warden-Ireland road, on the Southill parish boundary.[1] It crosses a small tributary stream of the Ivel. Although it lies a few miles from the Ivel Navigation, it is similar in design to the standard Navigation bridges erected in 1823, and is appropriately mentioned in this section. Its presence is probably due to the fact that the adjacent landowner, Lord Ongley of Old Warden, was a Navigation Commissioner. He may have taken advantage of the bridge-building activity on the Navigation to acquire a similar structure for his own property. It was recorded as King's bridge in 1888,[2] but has now been bypassed with a modern bridge lying to the west.

A 1710 perambulation of Old Warden parish mentions 'Fleett bridge' as one of the landmarks on the boundary with Southill.[3] This may have been a predecessor of King's bridge, on the same site.

NOTES
1   TL 130 430; HER 14134
2   Beds RO: QBP 9
3   Beds RO: X 248/65; CRT 130 WAR 3

SOME OTHER IVEL NAVIGATION BRIDGES

A footpath between Blunham and Tempsford crossed the Navigation by **High Ramper bridge.**[1] It was described in the *Lockgate* (1963): 'High Bamper [sic] ... rests on the original foundations and was used as a roving bridge.'[2] (A roving bridge is one which takes the towpath from one side of the watercourse to the other.) There is now a modern bridge on the site.

It has been suggested that there was an 1823 Moreton and Kinman standard navigation bridge at Sandy,[3] but no evidence to support this has been found.

Spur bridge[4] east of Moggerhanger, was shown on Jefferys' 1765 map of Bedfordshire, and may date from the first phase of the Navigation. The present bridge has a modern superstructure, which rests on original but much-repaired sandstone abutments.

NOTES
1   TL 154 525; HER 15759
2   M C Ewans, 'The Ivel Today: A Survey', *Lockgate* I no 6, Jan 1963, 91-96
3   *ibid,* 91
4   TL 160 496; HER 9788

THE GRAND JUNCTION CANAL

With the opening of the Duke of Bridgewater's canal between Worsley and Manchester in 1761, waterborne transport was no longer restricted to the natural river valleys. Tunnels were dug through hills, aqueducts erected over valleys, and extensive series of locks lifting boats to different levels all contributed to the success of the system. By the end of the 18th century a network of canals covered much of industrial England. However, the circuitous route from Birmingham to London via the Oxford canal to the Thames caused delays. In 1792 a new canal was proposed, the Grand Junction Canal, to run from Brentford on the Thames to Braunston on the Oxford Canal in Northamptonshire. Work began in 1793 and was completed in 1800, apart from the Blisworth tunnel which opened in 1805.[1]

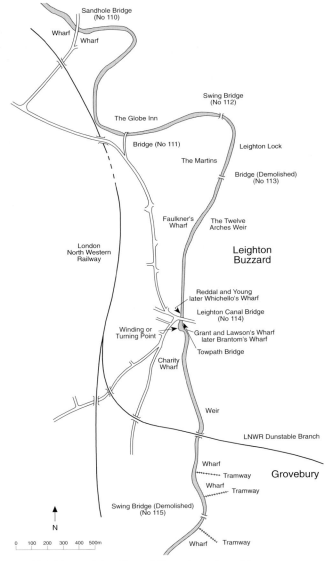

Fig 123 Map of the Grand Junction Canal in Bedfordshire (Drawing by Martin Cook)

Only a very small stretch of the canal passes through Bedfordshire, and then only because of changes to the county boundary in 1965 when Linslade parish was transferred from Buckinghamshire. The canal's course through Linslade posed few engineering problems. The artificial channel ran parallel to the River Ouzel and only one lock, Leighton lock, was needed in the 5.6km (3½ mile) stretch. Several bridges were built (numbers 110-115 on the canal), linking fields and roads which had been newly separated by the canal. There are no examples of 'roving' bridges on the Linslade stretch.

Of the six bridges on the Bedfordshire stretch only one, at Sandhole (bridge no 110), remains close to its original state.

The canal became known as the Grand Union Canal after 1929, when a number of canals were amalgamated to form the Grand Union Canal Ltd.[2]

NOTES
1 For a detailed history, see A H Faulkner, *The Grand Junction Canal,* 1972; see also Martin Cook & Peter McKeague, 'The Grand Junction Canal and its Bridges', *Beds Mag* 23 no 177, Summer 1991, 30-34
2 Faulkner, *op cit,* 212

SANDHOLE CANAL BRIDGE
Heath and Reach

Sandhole is a typical example of a Grand Junction canal bridge,[1] and was built c.1800 to carry the road from Heath and Reach to Linslade over the new canal. It has a single arch of yellow bricks, made from local gault clay, spanning both the canal, which narrows markedly under the arch, and the towpath. The bridge is set obliquely to the canal, and an elongated west abutment further emphasises its asymmetrical appearance (Fig 124). The arch ring is formed by alternating a single brick stretcher with two headers. There is protective ironwork guarding the relatively soft brick arrises of the lower arch walls on the north-east and south-east quoins adjacent to the towpath. Deep grooves worn into the guards testify to the strains of hauling the heavily laden barges through the constriction of the arch (Fig 125). Above the arch ring on both elevations, a plate with the Grand Junction Canal bridge number (no 110) may still be seen. There is a plain two-course brick string course supporting a brick parapet, which has square terminals capped in millstone grit.

The scant remains of a wharf, a stone-built quayside with a timber floor behind, survive to the south-west.

NOTES
1 SP 909 269; HER 4695

Fig 124 Sandhole canal bridge: south face (Beds Photographic Services)

Fig 125 Sandhole canal bridge: iron guard at north-east quoin, grooves worn by tow ropes (Beds Photographic Services)

LINSLADE CANAL BRIDGE

Grand Junction canal bridge no 114 carries the road between Linslade and Leighton Buzzard.[1] It was built in c.1800, but substantially reconstructed in 1845.[2] In 1881 an agreement was drawn up between the Parish of Linslade and the Grand Junction Canal Company for the parish to widen the roadway over the bridge.[3] This was in turn replaced in 1969 by a new carriageway resting on the earlier abutments.

The development of the canal had a stimulating effect on Leighton Buzzard and Linslade, as locally quarried sand could now be distributed along the canal network and beyond. Three wharves to handle the trade were built on the west bank of the canal, with a further wharf on the east bank. New industry grew up alongside the canal, including several lime kilns and other small factory sites. The growth in trade soon led to the development and expansion of Linslade around the wharves.

NOTES
1 SP 915 250; HER 11013
2 Bucks RO: BAS 695/28
3 Beds RO: CRT 130 LEI 19

Fig 126 Brantom's Wharf towpath bridge, Linslade (Beds Photographic Services)

BRANTOM'S WHARF TOWPATH BRIDGE, Linslade

South of Linslade canal bridge, on the east bank of the canal, a bridge carries the towpath over the inlet to the former Brantom's (originally Grant and Lawford's) Wharf.[1] It was built following an application by Grant in 1800 to construct a dock off the canal.[2]

The towpath bridge is built mainly of brick, with limestone quoins and a row of limestone blocks along the face at water level. It has a single rounded arch allowing access to the wharf for one barge. Two courses of brick form the string course below the parapet. The approach ramps are long and gentle, to allow for the easy passage of horses on the towpath.

The dock was infilled in 1973 but the bridge preserved.

NOTES
1   SP 915 249; HER 4793
2   A H Faulkner, *The Grand Junction Canal*, 1972, 98

SOME OTHER GRAND JUNCTION CANAL BRIDGES

Grand Junction canal bridge no 111, near the **Globe Inn,** north of Leighton Buzzard, retains its original abutments of red and yellow brick but has a later iron girder span.[1] **Bridge no 113** further south has been demolished.[2]

About 650m north of the canal bridge at Linslade, where a meander of the River Ouzel comes very close to the east side of the canal embankment, **Twelve Arches Weir** drains surplus water from the canal to the river. The twelve arches are of shallow elliptical form with a brick string course, and carry the towpath over the weir.[3]

There were two **Swing bridges** on the length of the Canal within Bedfordshire (this type of bridge pivoted horizontally to enable canal traffic to pass through). North of Linslade, swing bridge no 112 still survives though it is no longer in use.[4] No 115, south of Linslade has been removed, but its abutments are still visible.[5]

NOTES
1   SP 912 262; HER 6537
2   SP 918 259; HER 15712
3   SP 917 257; HER 15713
4   SP 918 263; HER 15710
5   SP 917 237; HER 15711

PARK BRIDGES

In the 18th century there was a move away from formalised parks and gardens towards the creation of more open natural landscapes with many water features. Fine classical-style bridges began to be built, to enhance the 'natural' landscapes in which they were set, and there are some interesting examples of this trend in Bedfordshire. They highlight the quality of architecture which was being commissioned for private schemes, at a period when rubble construction techniques were often still used for road bridges.

BASIN BRIDGE, Woburn Park

Basin bridge[1] is on the site of an earlier bridge erected in 1770-73 to a design by William Chambers. This was replaced in 1812-13 by Humphrey Repton as part of his alterations to the Park, although the balusters of the older bridge were re-used.[2] The present 'bridge' is actually a dam between two lakes on different levels; three arches are visible on the lower side towards Basin Pond, but their

Fig 127 Basin bridge, Woburn Park: north-west face, overlooking Basin Pond

upper ends are sealed with brickwork to retain the water from the higher lake to the south-east. The core of the structure is mainly of brick, and it was originally faced with Totternhoe clunch. It was re-faced with Portland stone in the late 19th century, and the voids behind the new stonework filled with a type of very strong cement

which was used experimentally in building works by the Bedford Estate in the 19th century.[3] The differential stresses caused by the cement, and the rusting of the iron clamps which held the facing stones in place, caused structural failure in recent years. The bridge was repaired and refaced by the Bedford Estate in 1992.[4]

NOTES
1. SP 962 324; HER 4948
2. Beds RO: CRT 130 WOBURN 33, History and description of bridge, by Marie P G Draper, Bedford Estate Archivist, 1980
3. J Caird, *English Agriculture in 1850-51,* 1852, reprinted 1967, 439
4. Access to the repair work was kindly made available by the Bedford Estate, through the architect Pamela Ward

SOME OTHER PRIVATE BRIDGES

It can be assumed that the large number of medieval moated sites in the county were equipped with bridges, but only a few are documented. Local traditions recall drawbridges at Moat Farm, Cranfield[1] and Upper Samshill, Westoning.[2] The earliest permanent moat bridge known to survive in Bedfordshire is at **Bletsoe Castle.** This is a late 16th century limestone rubble bridge with two pointed arches. It is of typical medieval form, though the parapets are later additions.[3]

'Smeaton's bridge' in Southill Park was probably built by Henry Holland in c.1800;[4] it is of red brick, with an ashlar face to the side overlooking the lake. **Wrest Park** contains a Chinese- style bridge, dating from 1876.[5] There is a fine collection of ornamental 19th century iron bridges in the **Swiss Garden,** Old Warden.[6]

Continuing this tradition into the 20th century, though in a public context, the Suspension bridge over the River Lea in **Wardown Park,** Luton was built c.1910.[7]

NOTES
1. SP 966 433; HER 49
2. TL 047 321; HER 3418
3. TL 024 583; HER 5565; Illustrated in J Fisher, *Collections Historical Genealogical and Topographical of Bedfordshire,* 59 no 17
4. TL 146 431; HER 5938
5. TL 093 351; HER 3780
6. TL 149 448; HER 12835, 12883-4)
7. TL 088 246; HER 15716; Luton Museum photo: LM/BI 911/29; J Dyer, F Stygall, J Dony, *The Story of Luton,* 1964, 178

BRIDGES IN THE PARISH - A CASE STUDY OF KEMPSTON

Major road bridges comprised only a small fraction of the river and stream crossings that must have existed throughout the medieval and later landscape. At a local level, whenever a road or footpath met a river or even a small stream it must have crossed by some means - ferry, ford, makeshift planks or permanent bridge - but rarely is much known of such features, through lack of survival and poor documentation. References may be found in minor place-names, court or coroner's rolls, presentments for repair and wills. Sometimes there is no more than a single mention in historic records, but where detailed research has been undertaken a fuller picture can be reconstructed.

The historic parish of Kempston is a particularly useful study area as it is drained by three streams flowing into the Great Ouse at its northern boundary. The documentary records have also been extensively studied by John Wood, yielding many references to bridges.[1] Nine can be identified by the mid-18th century and most of these were

Fig 128 Bridges and fords in Kempston parish, c.1800

documented before the mid-16th century.

Bridges over the Hardwick brook in the south-east of the parish are the earliest to be recorded. **Cow bridge** existed on the Elstow parish boundary by 1332[2] and **Kempston Hardwick bridge** by 1430 (see above).[3] **Fulbeckbridge** over the Little brook (a tributary of Hardwick brook) was recorded in a field name in c.1430 and 1434;[4] this is probably the same site as Sailor's bridge, which was known as Salisbridge in 1650,[5] Searles bridge in 1702[6] and Surles bridge in 1725.[7] **'Pickle bridge** furlong' was recorded in Hardwick Hill Field in c.1711 (known as **'Pikes bridge** furlong' in 1763),[8] and may refer to a bridge on the old track running south-east from Up End which was designated a public footpath at the time of Enclosure.[9]

Another stream flows across the centre of the parish to join the Great Ouse at Kempston Mill. It was crossed by **Bells bridge** at Bell End, first referred to in the church-wardens' accounts for 1741,[10] and by an unnamed bridge on the road between Keeley Green and Green End, shown on a pre-enclosure map of c.1802.[11]

North brook was crossed by **Parker's bridge** in 1462/63,[12] and in 1541 Alice Smith left 'to the reparations of the **North brege,** 20d'.[13] The pre-enclosure map also shows a crossing far upstream at Bourne End.[14]

The main Bedford to Newport Pagnell highway lies to the north of the parish, crossing the Great Ouse at **Bromham bridge,** but there were also lesser bridges across the loop of the river between Kempston and Biddenham. A footbridge at **Kempston Mill,** which the Abbess of Elstow was instructed to repair in 1436, spanned the mill channel.[15] Another, known as the **Long Plank,** continued the same footpath across the 'Old Ree' (the north arm of the river) to give access to Biddenham parish; in the 18th century, James Mobbs was ordered by the parish vestry to see to its repair.[16]

A short distance upstream of Kempston Mill the Ouse was crossed by what has been described as a paved Roman ford.[17] This was in fact the last remnants of a 17th century bridge built by the Cater family.[18] **'Sir Edward Cater's Great Bridge'** is first mentioned in a lease of 1666[19] allowing certain men to use the bridge for the carriage of grass and hay when the river was too high to ford. The fragmentary remains, which were visible until about 20 years ago, were the paved stone inverts protecting the base of the bridge from scour. The two rows of oak piles 18 ft (5.5m) apart were the remains of the bridge's timber uprights. It would appear to have been nothing more than an accommodation bridge linking the manor with pastures by the river.

Some bridges which do not lie on public roads have only been identified through field survey. A rubble lime-stone arch was discovered by Eric Compton in 1983 north of Kempston Hardwick.[20] It is of traditional local character, and difficult to date from its style, but it linked the Enclosure allotments which became Marshleys Farm[21]

and is probably 19th century in origin. A small stone bridge was recorded in 1978, by a spring at Bourne End.[22]

Despite these many bridges in the parish, not all roads were equally well served. There were fords across North brook to the north of the church, and **Rushy ford,** lying midway between Parker's bridge and North bridge, remained in use until the time of Enclosure in 1804.[23] There was another at West End Green, whilst the Wootton bourne appears to flow down the road from Keeley Green to Bell End in 1765.[24] In the east of the parish Ham ford connected Kempston with Ford End, Biddenham, across the Ouse.

A complex picture emerges of local communications. The explanation for such a varied pattern lies in the influence of local topography and the extent of local interest and finance. The need for bridges was greatest where stream banks were steep, trapping water in a deep channel in times of flood. In broader valleys shallow flood water could spread over a wider area, creating less of a barrier. Kempston demonstrates how the need of local communities for access to both local and long distance communication was met. To the north, Bromham bridge carried a major highway over the Ouse; many small bridges in the parish took local roads over the three streams; others, such as Cater's bridge, served simply for agricultural access.

NOTES

1   J Wood, *Kempston parish survey,* 1984
2   TL 042 472; HER 11730; *BHRS* (4vo) 3, 1929
3   Beds RO: PE 466/7/1
4   TL 026 463; HER 11687; Beds RO: PE 466/7/1; PE 466/1 m6, 7
5   Beds RO: PE 466/9
6   Beds RO: X 435/14-15
7   Beds RO: X 435/18
8   HER 11736; TL 034 464; Beds RO: X 435 uncat
9   Beds RO: MR 7, Draft Enclosure Map, c.1802
10 Beds RO: P 60/5/4
11 Beds RO: MR 7, Draft Enclosure Map, c.1802
12 SP 997 475; HER 11732; Beds RO: PE 466/1 m 9
13 TL 012 480; HER 11731; Beds RO: ABP/R 6 f78
14 SP 974 456; HER 15766
15 TL 023 477; HER 1081; Beds RO: PE 466/1
16 TL 018 478; HER 7278; Beds RO: P 60/8/1, Kempston Vestry minute books
17 R W Bagshawe, 'An Unrecorded Roman Ford', *Beds Mag* 6 no 42, Autumn 1957, 57-60; Viatores, *Roman Roads in the South-East Midlands,* 1964, 281-282; English Heritage Ancient Monument Record form, no 107
18 Wood, *op cit,* 24-26
19 TL 017 477; HER 814 ('Roman ford'); HER 11527 (Sir Edward Cater's Great Bridge); Beds RO: PE 362
20 TL 029 454; HER 15767
21 Beds RO: MA 18a, Book E, 1804
22 SP 968 452; HER 9188; field survey by R F White and A Allden for Beds County Council
23 Beds RO: MA 18a
24 Jefferys' Map of Bedfordshire, 1765

TECHNICAL SUMMARY

The character of individual bridges is determined by local transport needs and topography, the availability of raw materials and finance, the preference of the architect (if any), and the skill of the builders. Each phase of repair or alteration also reflects many of these varied influences. However, the study of bridges across the whole county of Bedfordshire makes it possible to draw out themes and trends in construction styles and techniques, both geographically and through time.

These themes are presented by discussing the various stages and elements of bridge construction.

CHOICE OF SITE

Many bridge sites replaced an existing ford, thereby taking advantage of the shallow water to enable good foundations to be laid, and avoiding the need to divert an established routeway. Where there is no evidence of a ford, but the crossing is clearly ancient, it is rarely possible to demonstrate when some form of bridge (even if only planks or tree trunks) was first provided. By medieval times, a new road crossing, such as that established when the town of Leighton Buzzard was laid out, was almost certainly furnished with a bridge from the outset.

The development of engineering skills in the 18th and 19th centuries enabled the choice of bridge site to be less dependent on physical constraints. Both Tempsford bridge on the Great North road (A1) and Prebend Street bridge in Bedford could be built at the place which was most convenient for the road; the depth and width of the river was not a prime consideration.

RAW MATERIALS

Timber

In the early middle ages, timber was the main material used for building construction, even in areas where stone was readily available. Major buildings, such as churches, were the first to be constructed in stone, and late Saxon work is found in St Mary's and St Peter's churches in Bedford and in a number of churches in the Ouse valley upstream.[1] It has been argued by Rigold that most major medieval bridges were of wooden construction until the 14th century.[2] Frequent references to wood in both medieval and later records, as well as topographical accounts and illustrations, tend to reinforce that view. However, by their very nature such wooden structures have left minimal visible physical evidence; it is often only by chance that any remains are discovered in excavations, such as those found at Monnow bridge at Monmouth,[3] or at Hemington in Leicestershire.[4]

Without doubt many of the older stone bridges replaced earlier wooden structures on or near the same site. On the Ouse, the early 15th century stone bridges at St Ives and Huntingdon probably replaced earlier timber structures,[5] whilst work on the first stone bridge at St Neots only began sometime after 1588.[6] However, vertical timbers found at Harrold and Bromham during recent underpinning are more likely to have been foundation piles for the later stone bridges than survivals from earlier timber structures. Many of the county's minor bridges were still of wood in the 16th century, such as the wooden bridge which was built at Brache near Luton in 1522.[7] But even as late as 1736 the first bridge across the River Ouse at Tempsford was of timber.[8] Of the lesser Ouse bridges, a descriptive name like Long Plank at Kempston is self-explanatory. Similar structures could also be expected at mill sites: at Oakley, Orlebar Marsh noted a very small wooden bridge 'covered with stone' in the early 19th century.[9]

Repairs using timber are well-documented. Bailiffs' accounts for Harrold show that arch 14 was planked over in 1532.[10] However, timber was more often used only as a temporary component in the construction or repair of bridges, particularly for the formation of arches, and this can lead to some ambiguity in the documentary record. For example, repairs to the west arch of Leighton bridge in 1611 included payments for planks, carpenters and carriage of timber from King's Wood to the bridge to make the arch;[11] this was probably to provide a timber formwork to support the construction of a stone arch. The timber may also have been used for foundations and scaffolding.

Timber plank carriageways are implied in a number of cases. The 1588 survey of St Neots bridge found that the 29 'arches' (timber spans) of the narrower part of the bridge rested on a stone foundation.[12] The foot causeway at Turvey was largely constructed of 'openings covered with planks'.[13]

Wooden railings were used on many bridges as late as the 19th century; traces of timber joists from these can still be seen at Harrold.

There is little direct documentary evidence of the sources of timber supply. By early post-medieval times, the distribution of ancient woodland in Bedfordshire was concentrated on the poorer soils of the Greensand ridge and in a parallel band across the clay ridges of the north-west of the county (Fig 129). Problems of supply away from these areas are highlighted by early post-medieval accounts. In particular, timber for the reconstruction work proposed for St Neots bridge in 1588 was transported considerable distances: 20 tons (20.3 tonnes) of timber were to be supplied from the manorial woods at Warden, some 12 miles (19 km) distant, 20 tons from the royal woods at Somersham 22 miles (35 km) away in Cambridgeshire, and another 88 tons (89.4 tonnes) from privately owned woods about 18 miles (30 km) to the north-east in Huntingdonshire. Huntingdonshire men were charged with transporting 153 tons (155.4 tonnes) of

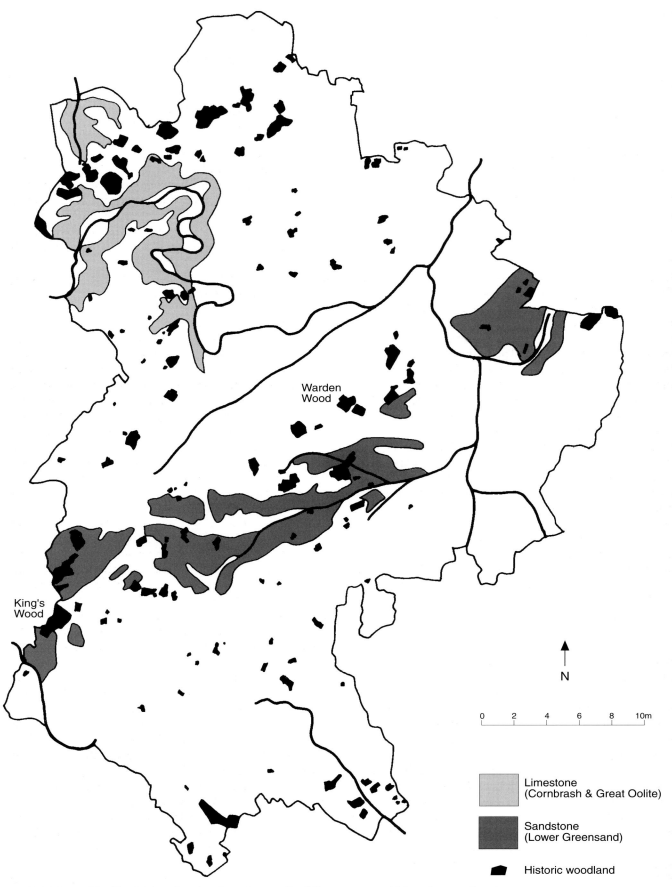

King's
Wood

Warden
Wood

N

| 0 | 2 | 4 | 6 | 8 | 10m |

Limestone
(Cornbrash & Great Oolite)

Sandstone
(Lower Greensand)

Historic woodland

Fig 129 Map of Bedfordshire showing locations of building stone and historic woodland

timber for £61 4s 0d, which was a considerable sum for carriage.

Stone

Building stone is found in three areas in the county. Limestone from the north-west and sandstone from the Greensand Ridge across mid-Bedfordshire were both quarried for building stone over a long period until the 20th century (Fig 129). A hard chalk known as Totternhoe clunch was quarried and mined in localised areas in the south of the county. It was primarily used for decorative work on major buildings such as churches. It erodes easily and is therefore unsuitable for major construction work, though it provided the original facing stone for Basin bridge, Woburn.

Limestone

Limestone is exposed in the river valleys of north-west Bedfordshire. The lowest deposit in the sequence – the inferior oolite – occurs occasionally, but the higher Blisworth limestones of the Great Oolite form the principal exposure. This in turn is overlain by cornbrash in the sides of the river valley. These limestones are thinly bedded, which inhibits their use as freestone; they are more commonly used as rubble building stone. Generally only the Blisworth limestone was quarried, though pits at Biddenham and Harrold exploited the cornbrash. The quarry pits owned by Bromham chantry chapel give one of the few medieval references, but there are likely to have been stone pits in most parishes in the upper Ouse valley. These supplied the needs of the immediate locality, as well as major projects such as churches and bridges in other parishes or towns which lacked suitable building stone.

Records of repairs to Bromham bridge in the 19th century provide rare evidence about the use of local limestone. The Quarter Sessions minuted a delay 'because they have not until quite lately begun to quarry the harder kind of stone in the Bromham pits which we have been waiting for'.[14]

Sandstone

Sandstone occurs as intermittent (and rather unpredictable) deposits at various levels throughout the Greensand ridge.[15] Three principal areas of extraction have been identified: at Sandy Heath in the north-east, the Clophill and Silsoe area in mid-Bedfordshire and at Leighton Heath in the south-west. Doubtless there were many other local pits along the entire length of the ridge. Medieval and 17th century accounts confirm that extraction was sporadic and ill-organised. On the heaths in Leighton parish extraction of raw materials was closely controlled by the manor court. The court rolls contain several references to fines being exacted, for example in 1394 'for digging soil and taking stones from the heath at Leighton without the licence of the Lord or his Officers'.[16]

Quarrying seems to have been relatively common in the Leighton Buzzard district during the post-medieval period, for numerous pits of all kinds are recorded, particularly in field names. There are references to quarry pits in 1490[17] at the East End, in 1494[18] at Lockyns Croft in Grovebury Field south of the town, and at an unknown location in 1602-38.[19] By the 19th century it is clear that the custom of digging stones and sand on the heaths had gone on for some time without payment or compensation to the lord of the manor. Poor men apparently regularly dug sandstone and sold it, as a right that was not challenged, whilst many others dug stone to build cottages.[20]

At Clophill, pits were dug over the common in the 17th century in search of stone, but it was very much a small-scale effort.[21] On Sandy Heath extraction continued on a localised piecemeal basis until about the 18th century when the stone sources began to be more regularly exploited. This is reflected in a marked increase in the number of structures built in local sandstone, including Tempsford and Girtford bridges.

The chronology of stone use

The distribution of ancient stone bridges is closely related to local geology and the availability of stone. There is a long tradition of limestone construction in the Ouse valley of north-west Bedfordshire, so not surprisingly the earliest documented and impressive stone bridges are found here, notably Turvey, Harrold, Stafford and Bromham. Each of these bridges is within a close distance of good stone supplies. 18th and 19th century limestone bridges at Radwell, Oakley and Felmersham lie within the same area. With occasional exceptions these bridges are entirely rubble-built, reflecting the character of the local stone and the quarrying methods.

Medieval stone bridges existed at Sutton in the 13th century and at Langford and Arlesey. Those which survive (Arlesey and Sutton) are in local sandstone, and it can be assumed that sandstone was used in the construction of other early stone bridges in the area, such as Clifton, Girtford, Shefford and Biggleswade. The 18th and early 19th century bridges over the Flit and Ivel are also built from local sandstone. In the Ouzel valley sandstone from Heath, north of Leighton Buzzard, was used to repair Slapton bridge in 1611.[22]

On the River Ouse downstream from Bedford the construction of stone bridges was a relatively late development, most probably due to the distance from the stone supply. The use of different stone sources is well documented at Barford bridge. 17th century accounts show that limestone was brought from Biddenham and sandstone from Sandy Heath; in the 18th century Harrold and Pavenham supplied limestone. The use of the two stones types was partly decorative, though transportation of stone from Harrold some 15 miles (24 km) away suggests that the limestone (harder wearing than sandstone) was needed for a specific purpose like pitching or invert construction.

During the post-medieval period stone began to imported from further afield. The 17th century bridge at

St Neots was built of stone from Ketton and Barnack near Stamford in Lincolnshire, about 35 miles (56 km) away.[23] Ketton also appeared at Sutton as an ashlar extension to the parapets in phase 3, tentatively dated to the late 17th century. Elsewhere odd blocks of fine oolitic limestone, possibly from Ketton or somewhere close by, appear to have been used for repairs. This is most noticeable at Barford, Blunham and Harrold bridges. Mid-19th century repairs to Bromham bridge even incorporate some clunch. Such repairs are undated, and the casual reuse of stone in bridges is a frequent and widespread occurrence.

More deliberate and careful use of stone can be seen in the few architecturally designed bridges in the county. Developments in engineering techniques, as well as in transport and communications, led to the use of imported harder wearing stone (Portland stone and Bramley Fall stone) for the main structural components (arches, string courses and parapet copings) at both Bedford and Tempsford. The remainder of the bridge at Tempsford was constructed from locally supplied sandstone, though it was cut in more substantial blocks than hitherto seen. At Bedford, Weldon stone from Northamptonshire was used in preference to local rubble limestone as facing stone for the spandrels.

During the 20th century, local stone quarries went out of use. As a result, Portland stone was regularly used for repairs until the 1970s, and can easily be picked out in many of the stone parapets by its white colour and blocky appearance. Since the early 1980s, encouraged by the requirements of ancient monuments legislation, more sympathetic materials have been used, in particular limestone from a series of quarries on the Lincolnshire/Northamptonshire border. Limited quantities of sandstone have been locally available from Clophill, though often it is too small for some of the more monolithic blocks used at Barford and Tempsford. Waste stone from sand quarries on Sandy Heath matches the colour and texture of stone at Tempsford and Girtford, but is rarely adequate for structural repairs. Occasionally deposits of good quality sandstone are encountered in quarries at Heath and Reach near Leighton Buzzard. Bramley Fall stone is still available as a replacement for damaged features at Tempsford and was used to repair the string course at Barford.

Brick

By the mid-18th century, most parishes in Bedfordshire supported at least one brick-kiln, though the use of bricks in construction was still mainly limited to buildings for the wealthy. Indeed the first known brick bridge in the county, Smeaton's bridge at Cardington dating from 1778, was privately financed by Samuel Whitbread.

After the removal of the Brick Tax in 1850, and in response to the growing demands for new housing, the brick industry flourished in the late 19th century,[24] and most minor road bridges and culverts of this period are brick-built. Brick was regularly used on major bridges for repairs and widenings (perhaps most impressively at Barford), and for parapets. A transition from stone to brick can be seen at Harrold, where the widening of 1879 was in limestone but with brick arch rings.

Iron

The first iron bridge was erected by Abraham Darby at Coalbrookdale, Shropshire in 1779 (now known as Ironbridge Gorge). After initial hesitation other examples followed, at first in the industrial north and then in the large cities. Rural areas were slower to adopt the idea; Tickford bridge at Newport Pagnell, Buckinghamshire, erected in 1810, is a notable exception.[25]

Most of Bedfordshire's early iron bridges were extremely simple. They were invariably of single span and basic in design. They relied on the principle of the timber beam rather than the stone arch, though the iron beams were slightly curved in order to distribute weight to the abutments. The earliest was built at Langford in 1819, followed by Broom in 1822. They were cast at Coalbrookdale in sections and transported by the Grand Junction Canal to Linford Wharf near Newport Pagnell, and thence by road to be assembled on site.

The standard Ivel Navigation bridges of 1823 were manufactured locally, by Moreton and Kinman of Biggleswade.[26] The two bridges in Shefford were manufactured in the town by Walker and Yeats in 1828, and Hyde bridge, in Luton Hoo Park, was supplied by Barwell and Hagger of Northampton in 1831.

Ironwork was also used occasionally for repairs and details on other bridges. At Barford iron tie-rods (made by Baker and Co of Bedford) were used to brace the bridge in 1897, and the iron copings on the east parapet were cast in Northampton.

Mortar and cement

Until the last hundred years, bridges have been built and repaired using lime mortar; this was prepared from lime (rendered down from limestone in kilns) mixed with aggregate (locally quarried sand and gravel). In the late 19th century cement began to be available commercially, and for much of the 20th century hard cement mortar was used for repairs and repointing. This was much stronger than the surrounding stone, and as a result the effects of erosion and differential stresses became concentrated on the fabric of the stone, causing serious decay. The effects of this were particularly severe at Basin bridge, Woburn and at Felmersham, where neat cement was used in late 19th and early 20th century repairs.

In modern repointing and stonework repairs only a small cement component is used, to assist with setting.

THE GROUND PLAN

The plans of bridges have been influenced over time by a variety of factors. In early periods, the prime constraint was the topography of the watercourse and its associated valley, though the importance of the route also affected the scale of the work undertaken. In later periods, the

109

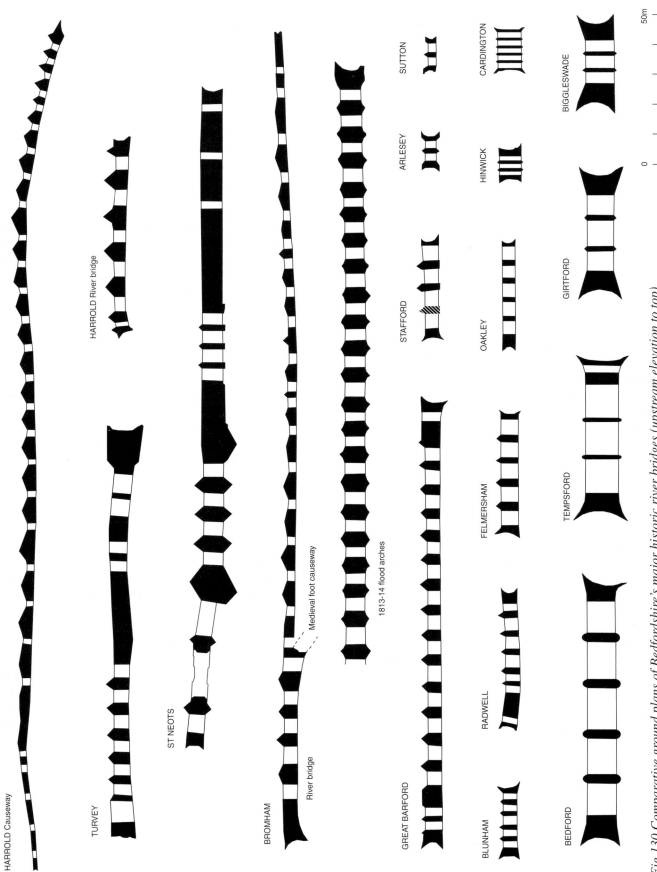

Fig 130 Comparative ground plans of Bedfordshire's major historic river bridges (upstream elevation to top)

development of engineering skills is reflected in the way key elements in bridge planning changed, particularly the relative sizes of piers and arches. For comparison, the ground plans of all the major bridges are shown together at the same scale in Figure 130.

Width and length

The width of medieval bridges was determined primarily by whether or not they were designed to be used by vehicles. Sutton bridge and the long causeways in the upper Ouse valley, at about 6-8 ft (2.0-2.5m), were wide enough only for horses or pedestrians; other traffic had to use the ford at Sutton, or cross the Ouse flood meadows at ground level. Early road bridges were only wide enough for one vehicle, because the volume of traffic (when balanced against the cost of bridge construction) did not warrant a two-way system. Even later bridges in the upper Ouse valley, such as Radwell and Oakley which were both built in traditional medieval style, were only 12 ft 6 in (3.8m) wide. On the other hand, Girtford at 29 ft 6 in (7.8m) and Tempsford at 30 ft 10 in (9.4m), both on the busy Great North road, accommodated more modern standards of design and allowed for two-way traffic.

The length of a bridge was determined not just by the width of the watercourse, but whether provision was made to cross the adjacent flood plain. Here the great medieval bridges of the upper Ouse valley were particularly distinctive, with their long foot causeways or 'causeys'. Stafford causeway stretched about 1250 ft (380m) from the river bank. The only causeway which survives is at Harrold, probably because access for vehicles was upgraded in the late middle ages when the part nearest the river was widened, and no further improvement was considered necessary.

In later periods, better provision was made for vehicles to cross the flood plains. Barford bridge was extended for this purpose in the late 17th/early 18th century, and Stafford, Bromham and Turvey foot causeways were all replaced by road bridges or causeways in the 19th century. Tempsford bridge of 1820 was equipped with a group of 7 flood arches on both sides, carrying the same road width as the river bridge.

Pier:arch ratio

The number of arches on medieval bridges seems to have been a compromise between the need to allow the passage of water and the desire to minimise the technically demanding effort of arch construction. For this reason, piers were often constructed on a massive scale, far more substantial than was necessary to take the loads exerted on them at the time. In effect, early bridges were sometimes more like causeways, punctuated by arches to allow the passage of water. The arches were structurally independent of one another, as can particularly be seen at Harrold where they were all separately maintained.

Comparing the pier thickness against the arch span forms a basis for comparing the 'crudely' built medieval structures with later architecturally designed bridges. A number of continental publications from the Renaissance through to the early 18th century analysed pier:arch ratios in classical and later architecture. Serlio observed that ancient Roman bridges had a ratio of 1:2, and in 1553 Alberti recommended 1:3 as ideal. Palladio (1570) favoured proportions which were between 1:4 and 1:6 whilst Gautier suggested a ratio of 1:5 for spans greater than 20 ft (6m).[27]

The medieval river bridges in Bedfordshire rarely reach even ancient Roman proportions. On average, the river arches at Harrold and Bromham are no larger than the intervening piers (a ratio of about 1:1); the main river arches at Turvey are slightly larger proportionally, but it is only the bridge at Stafford which seems to have reached the classical pier:arch ratio of 1:2.

In comparison, bridges over the narrower Ivel and its tributaries were generally better proportioned than those over the upper Ouse, as were the 17th century bridges at Blunham and St Neots. Arlesey, Langford and Sutton, although they have a pier:arch ratio of less than 1:2, still display a well-balanced unity of design.

Among the rest of the county's bridges, pier:arch ratios are fairly consistent until the 19th century. They range from Barford at 1:1.3 to Cardington at 1:1.8 (even though the latter was an architect designed bridge). The exception was the great 17th century central arch of St Neots at 1:2.5. At the beginning of the 19th century, the new engineering techniques and architectural design began to have an impact. Bedford, Biggleswade and Girtford bridges, and the turnpike arches at Turvey are nearer 1:4. Tempsford is outstanding at nearly 1:8, confirming the extremely high quality of its architecture.

Substantial piers continued to be a tradition in the upper Ouse valley into the 19th century. At Bromham, Salmon's causeway piers match the solidness of medieval river piers. Radwell and Felmersham bridges also have massive piers, although in other respects (such as cutwater design) more modern techniques were reflected. The pier:arch ratio shows that these local bridges were still very much in the medieval mould.

Harrison has pointed out that the typical arch span of Southern England is markedly less than the medieval bridge in the north of the country.[28] The difference in spans may partly reflect local topographical circumstances (with narrower river valleys in the north), but the main factor is that of date. The northern bridges, such as Twizel quoted by Harrison, generally belong to the late medieval period whereas many of the southern bridges would appear to be much older. Certainly the first large span in Bedfordshire dates from the early 17th century with the construction of St Neots bridge.

PIERS

Preparing the foundation

In the course of recent repair schemes, there have been few opportunities to examine bridge foundations. In many cases, river piers had already been surrounded by concrete slabs twenty or thirty years ago, to line and protect the river bed; the work had usually gone unrecorded. The evidence that has been recovered more recently allows some general conclusions about foundation design to be drawn.

Part of the skill of medieval bridge builders was their understanding of the nature of the ground on which they were working, and their ability to support massive stone structures with apparently very slight foundations. The basic principle adopted was to excavate down to a stable base, and then to spread the load of the bridge over a broad area. Width and overall stability were considered more important than depth. When Harrold bridge was underpinned in 1988-89, it was found that this level base consisted of compacted clay which was often no more than 200-300mm (8-12 in) beneath the top of the river silts. At Sutton, sandstone bedrock was encountered immediately below the bed of the stream.

There are no documentary references to the use of dams when building Bedfordshire's medieval bridges. In most cases, where a bridge was constructed on a broad, shallow ford site, it would have been a simple matter to dam off part of the flow at a time to build each pier.

Once the loose river silts were removed, and a stable foundation level reached, timber was then employed to give structural support. Few timber foundations have been recorded, and although a number of vertical timbers were located during underpinning work at Harrold, these almost certainly relate to later repairs. It is likely that piles were driven into the clay to form a base for the stonework, both in the original construction and during repairs and alterations. During demolition of the old Bedford bridge in 1811, George Cloake observed that 'the Foundations of all the Piers which have hitherto been taken down were built upon Piles, about 3 ft [0.9m] long, driven through a stratum of Clay, lying on a Rock of solid Stone'.[29] This indicates a bridge built directly on timber piles which were driven down as far as solid bedrock. The 13th century elm foundation raft from Sutton bridge is a rare form. The four parallel timbers take the weight of the whole bridge from abutment to abutment; this technique was clearly only possible over a narrow stream. In any case, the solid sandstone on the river bed would have prevented the use of vertical piles. The foundations for timber bridges usually consisted of a series of parallel sole plates supporting the trestles, which performed the same function as piers in a stone bridge in carrying the arches. Often these plates were joined by cross beams to form a more rigid structure. Fisher's illustration of Tempsford (Fig 12)[30] is the only record of such a bridge in the county, but the details of the structure are not clear. The bridge at Brache, Luton, must have been of similar form.

Evidence for the use of timber in the foundations of post-medieval bridges is occasionally preserved in contract drawings and instructions. Those for Tempsford bridge are particularly precise, and involved the use of iron-tipped piles supporting a rigid grating infilled with rammed stone to form a level building platform. Similar detailed instructions are given for the 1838 reconstruction of Horsepool bridge, Luton (Fig 112).

Stone footings

Generally medieval piers rose vertically or had a single offset or step at the base. Multiple offsets seem to be a late feature; at Harrold triple offsets are associated with late 19th century repairs, and a quintuple offset built over elaborate timber shoring at pier 11/12 was almost certainly late, and introduced in response to scouring of the arch walls.

Contract drawings again provide useful information for the later bridges. Wing's bridge at Bedford had triple offsets whilst the 1902 widenings to Bromham river arches are drawn as quintuple offsets (though shown as quadruple in plan). Similarly the 1899 alteration to the middle flood arch of Stafford embankment rested on a quadruple offset. The effect of the offset was to spread the load of the pier over a greater area, a function which was performed much more gracefully by the gently broadening piers employed by Savage at Tempsford. Here the piers were 12 ft (3.7m) wide at the base reducing in a curve to only 6 ft (1.8m) at the arch springing.

The cutwaters and basal courses of arches beneath the springing are vulnerable to the erosive power of water especially in flood. This is particularly true of the sandstone bridges in the east of the county. The river piers at Barford have been patched at and above water level on many occasions. Sometimes a more deliberate effort was made to protect the stonework. For instance, at Sutton the main body of both the abutments and pier have been protected by narrow plinths, which were not original features; variations in stone type and size demonstrate their later date. The west side of the pier at Arlesey bridge has similarly been repaired. In 1983 the piers at Radwell bridge were encased in a broad limestone plinth above the water line. These plinths not only corrected the problem of decayed stonework but offered additional protection to the piers from debris washed downstream. The incorporation of plinths as part of the original design first occurs in the county during the late 18th century when Smeaton drew up his plans for the bridge in Cardington. Even then this technique was not universally adopted and on most bridges the piers still carried straight down to the foundations.

CUTWATERS

Medieval builders were aware of the need for projecting cutwaters on the upstream face of piers. Apart from channelling the water through the arches, they offered protection to the faces of the piers from the force of the current and debris carried downstream by the water. The downstream face was often left unprotected and open to the worst effects of scour from eddying, or at best had a square ended projection on the downstream face. None of the surviving medieval Ouse bridges in Bedfordshire had

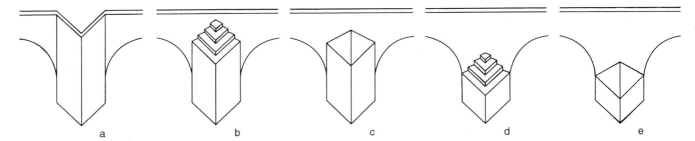

Fig 131 Some basic cutwater types: a) medieval keeled cutwater to full height; b) & c) truncated cutwaters with stepped and half-pyramid caps; d) & e) cutwaters capped at arch springing

downstream cutwaters, though late 18th century illustrations of Bedford bridge show rectangular projections against the downstream elevation. The piers either side of arch 11 at Harrold also project slightly from the original build, perhaps as means of protection.

The absence of downstream cutwaters generally continues in post-medieval bridges, though triangular cutwaters on the downstream elevation appear at St Neots in the late 16th/early 17th century. The three early 19th century bridges on the Ouse – Tempsford, Bedford and the flood arches at Bromham – each had cutwaters on both faces. These were architect designed structures at a period when bridge engineering was advancing rapidly, but bridges in the local style continued to be built with upstream cutwaters only as at Felmersham and Radwell, whilst cutwaters were absent altogether at Oakley. By way of comparison, Huntingdon and St Ives bridges, downstream of St Neots, have cutwaters on both faces, whilst the only surviving medieval bridge upstream, at Thornborough in Buckinghamshire, does not.

On the Ivel and its tributaries, Sutton had a cutwater on the upstream face only whilst Arlesey bridge had pointed cutwaters on both faces. In the 18th century the newly built bridges at Girtford and Biggleswade on the Ivel, and Chicksands and Clophill on the Flit, had cutwaters on both faces, reflecting developments elsewhere in the country.

The development of cutwater styles, summarised in Figure 131, can be charted by studying the design of Bedfordshire bridges over time. The descriptive classification follows is that proposed by Renn in his study of the Wey bridges in Surrey.[31]

Medieval to 17th century

Upstream cutwaters as seen on Sutton or Turvey bridges are typical of the period. They are keeled (triangular in plan) to the full height of the bridge, forming pedestrian refuges (Renn style II). To some extent the form persisted into the 19th century, when the cutwaters on Salmon's rebuilding of the Bromham causeway rose the full height of the bridge to form refuges, but unlike the earlier medieval examples the apex of each cutwater has a more rounded profile.

The shape and appearance of early cutwaters were frequently altered when bridges were widened, or parapets added. In this respect only the upstream face of Harrold causeway has been left in its original form; after the river bridge was widened its cutwaters were capped at road level with low pyramidal top. When the foot causeway near the river was widened to form the flood arches the medieval cutwaters were almost entirely masked by irregular rounded buttresses. At Stafford the stepped top was clearly added after the bridge had been widened in the 19th century. Similarly the Blunham cutwaters were altered with the addition of elaborate cappings, after the parapets were heightened.

18th and 19th centuries

There is a much greater variation in style from the 18th century. Keeled cutwaters no longer rose the full height of the bridge but were capped at the arch springing in a variety of forms. It is not clear exactly where these changes originated but classical designs were appearing in England by the mid-17th century. The balustraded Clare College bridge built in 1640 at Cambridge is perhaps amongst the earliest of the new forms. Here the cutwater no longer rises the full height of the bridge but the apex is chamfered back almost to the face of the bridge before rising vertically as a pilaster. It is an early example in England of stopping the cutwater before the road level, a form which was to be developed in the following centuries.

The main 18th century forms are in essence variations of the same theme. Renn's style V, the keeled forms with half pyramid cappings occur at Kempston Hardwick and formerly on the upstream face of Biggleswade bridge. This was also the form favoured by Smeaton in his rather conservatively designed bridge at Cardington. Both Radwell and Felmersham are similar but have stepped rubble limestone caps, a form which is also seen at Hinwick and Chicksands. Both pyramid and stepped caps were later to be used on the alterations to Harrold and Stafford bridges respectively.

The similarity between Biggleswade and Girtford bridges was reflected in their cutwater design. Half-pyramid caps occur at the level of the arch springing on both faces of Girtford, and on the upstream face of Biggleswade. The main difference between the two is that the arch springing at Girtford is at the water line (corresponding to Renn style VI), whereas the piers and their keeled cutwaters at Biggleswade are raised to a higher level (style V).[32] On the downstream face of Biggleswade bridge, the cutwaters are again keeled to the arch springing, but instead of the half pyramid capping the tops are chamfered.

Bedfordshire was slow in adopting new forms and designs. It was not until the early 19th century that the basic cutwater shape began to change within the county. Instead of the keeled form of triangular plan a rounded form was introduced by Wing at Bedford, and the traditional half pyramid was replaced by a domed cap. At Tempsford, Savage preferred the traditional form but with slightly convex faces rather like the profile of a boat. They were finished with similarly shaped stepped capstones. The same form of a boat-shaped keeled cutwater, though in a much simpler fashion, was to be used by Webster for the piers to Cauldwell bridge (Prebend Street) in Bedford over 60 years later.

ARCHES

Construction
The very plain forms of most of the surviving medieval arches in Bedfordshire argues for the simplest methods of construction. Crude timber falsework or centering and scaffolding was constructed, probably similar to that which Renn suggests had been used to build bridges on the River Wey in Surrey[33] (although the arch form in Bedfordshire was much smoother and more rounded than the irregular arches of the Wey bridges). A slightly different technique may have been adopted for the ribbed arches of Bedford, Stafford and St Neots; here the ribbing may have been constructed first on individual formwork and then the rubble arch soffit formed behind.

Each arch was built around individually constructed centering; this would not necessarily be identical in shape

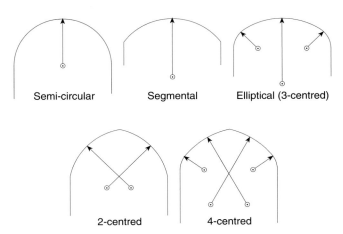

Fig 133 The geometry of the main arch shapes

and size from one arch to the next, leading to irregularity in appearance. Repeated stories of collapse and rebuild at various bridges highlight the technical difficulties of arch construction. Arch 14 of Harrold bridge collapsed in 1532, and was not rebuilt until the 1840's; a timber carriageway sufficed for over three centuries. At Barford, two river arches (12 and 13) collapsed and had to be rebuilt in 1781,[34] and one of the late 17th/early 18th century flood arches (arch 5) in 1753.[35] Whilst in some cases destruction may have been caused by flood damage, this last example almost certainly occurred as a result of removing the centre at the wrong time. The main problems are summarised by Renn. If the centering was removed too late there was a danger that the arch would become too rigid and overstressed in places. The resulting brittleness would lead to collapse when the arch was unable to adjust to the slight movement caused by removing the centering. On the other hand if the supports were taken away whilst the mortar was still setting, slippage and collapse of the arch soffit could again result. Perhaps the badly formed and twisted character of the downstream side of Arch 12 at Harrold was caused in this manner (Fig 132).

Arch shape
The shape of an arch can be analysed by determining the radius of the arcs which form its curves, and the point (or centre) from which each radius springs (Fig 133). The simplest form is part (either half or less) of a circle, with the radius springing from only one centre. The use of two or four intersecting arcs, each arising from a different centre, gives a pointed arch.

There was no standard size and shape for arches in Bedfordshire bridges during the medieval period, and few of them can be dated on architectural features alone. The exceptions are finer arches like Sutton, which Jervoise[36] assigned to the 14th century but was shown through radiocarbon dating to be mid- to late 13th century. The fine double-ordered ironstone arch at Harrold (arch 11) may be 15th century in date whilst the broad chamfered

Fig 132 Harrold bridge: east face of arch 12, showing distortion of arch ring

arrises at Blunham river bridge are thought to be 17th century.[37] Ribbed arches are (or were, for none now survive) a medieval form from the late 12th century which persisted in Bedfordshire through to the 17th century at St Neots.

Both pointed and rounded arches were used by medieval builders, though styles were not normally mixed on the same bridge, even when different parties were involved with maintenance. Where different styles do occur it can be the result of reconstruction, as at Harrold arch 11. The surviving medieval arches at Turvey are exclusively pointed, whereas Bromham, Bedford, and phase 1 of Barford all had rounded arches. Stafford river bridge is unusual in showing both round and pointed arches (Fig 51).

In Harrold foot causeway the first nine arches, later widened for road traffic, are rounded, but the remaining medieval arches, perhaps constructed later, are all pointed. Of the other causeways, only Bromham seems to have had rounded arches. Fisher shows Stafford causeway with pointed arches and the surviving fragments of the Turvey causeway also suggest some pointed arches (although most of the Turvey causeway consisted of no more than planks resting on stone piers).

Few of the medieval Ivel bridges survive, but both Sutton and Arlesey bridges have pointed arches, as apparently did Langford. The rounded arch form does not appear in any Ivel bridge until the almost semi-circular 17th century arches at Blunham river bridge.

Elliptical (three-centred) arches came into use with the development of engineering techniques in the 18th and 19th centuries; notable Bedfordshire examples are Girtford and Bedford.

Voussoirs

Medieval arch rings were usually constructed with a single row, or order, of stones, though double orders were also used in both medieval and post-medieval bridge construction. The use of this second 'counter' arch must have given added strength though even the single order limestone arch rings were of very strong proportions. The double-ordered arch was generally discarded as an architectural form during the 18th century, as the strengths of the single order were fully appreciated and exploited.

The shape and quality of voussoirs also varied. Some were no more than rectangular limestone blocks pitched round the arch with little attempt at regularity. This can be seen particularly in Harrold causeway (Fig 134), where the arch stones are simply the outer stones of courses which continued right through the arch soffit; there was no distinct arch ring as such. In other arches the voussoirs were more precisely set radially to the arch, and perhaps cut into a wedge shape. The highest quality of work could be seen for example at Sutton, where the voussoirs were accurately cut, with very tight joints between them (see Fig 94).

From the 18th century all the bridges designed by architects had single order arch rings, often with a projecting keystone. Their greater strength lay in the more

Fig 134 Harrold causeway: rubble limestone arch and walling

precise use of accurately shaped voussoirs but particularly in a better understanding of how bridges worked structurally. Even so the double ordered arch ring lingered on in repairs or alterations to many of the older bridges, as at Barford phase 3 (arch 17) and arch 14 at Harrold.

Where sandstone was in use, there was a tendency over time to introduce more massive voussoir stones into the arch rings, as at Blunham river bridge. At Barford the quality of voussoir stones begins to degenerate in the 18th or 19th century. Whereas before the stone was carefully cut into wedges, either rubble limestone was used in a most irregular fashion, or new rings were constructed from massive sandstone blocks the length of three to four voussoirs.

Often the traces of chamfers may still be found on the exposed arrises of voussoirs. These range from about 1.2 in (30mm) on 19th century arches at Bromham, to 5 in (130mm) on Harrold arch 11. The curved 'cornes de vache' at Tempsford (Fig 16) are an unusual feature designed to allow the smooth flow of water through the arch in times of flood. Decoration otherwise is limited to the fascia grooves at Hinwick and V-shaped slots between the voussoirs at Bedford (Fig 135).

Fig 135 Bedford bridge: voussoirs and ashlar walling

Fig 136 Girtford bridge: keystones

in arches 13 and 15 at Harrold, but the sharp quality of the tooling suggests that these have been refaced.

One situation in which limestone was finely dressed was in the three Ouse bridges which had ribbed arches, Stafford, Bedford and St Neots. Ribbing occurs on bridges from the late 12th century to the 18th century.[38] A late 12th or 13th century date might be appropriate for Bedford bridge, whilst the broad ribs at Stafford also suggest a medieval date. The ribbed arches at St Neots were probably built in the early 17th century, but the cross ribbing here is a very unusual feature.[39] In all three bridges the ribs were dressed stone with broad chamfers. The ribs were functional, pooling and directing the downward thrust of the arches, and perhaps allowing either a greater span to be bridged, or the use of inferior material in the remainder of the soffit.

WALLING

Once the piers and arches were in place, the spandrels were faced in stone up to road level. Usually the stonework was regularly coursed. In particular sandstone was almost always cut and used as dressed stone in bridges, and it is unusual to find irregular masonry in sandstone, except in repairs. The regular dressed blocks (Fig 137) at Sutton argue for abundant stone supply and

The use of keystones appears from the 17th century onwards. The earliest known Bedfordshire example was at St Neots where the cross rib at the top of the arch projected out forming the keystone; other cross ribs extended out at the haunch (halfway up the arch). Very badly eroded keystones can be seen at Blunham river bridge, flanked by slightly projecting stones, and similar features survive at Girtford (Fig 136). Single keystones are present at Bedford, Cardington, Tempsford, Hinwick and Oakley South. None of the other limestone bridges of this period, including the main river arches at Oakley, have keystones.

Soffits

Behind the face of an arch, the quality of stonework in the arch soffit was mainly determined by the type of stone used. Sandstone could be dressed with precision, as can be seen at Sutton, where the 13th century bridge has remarkably fine soffits of squared stones with very tight joints. Later sandstone bridges at Barford, Blunham and Girtford show similar workmanship. Northamptonshire ironstone, which was used in arch 11 at Harrold, has similar properties, as have Portland stone and Bramley Fall stone, used in the 19th century at Bedford and Tempsford respectively.

On the other hand, although limestone can be finely worked, its tendency to split along close bedding planes lends it more to use as rubble or roughly squared stone than as dressed stone (which involves a lot of waste). There is therefore no noticeable improvement in the quality of limestone soffits over time. Indeed, the most finely dressed arches can be seen in the medieval part of Bromham bridge, arches 23-26 (particularly 24 and 25). By contrast, Turvey's medieval arches are in rubble limestone, as also are arches 10 and 12 at Harrold (probably in near original condition). Similar rubble stonework can be seen in the later bridges at Radwell and Felmersham, and in arch 14 at Harrold which dates from the mid-19th century. There are more regular squared limestone soffits

Fig 137 Sutton bridge: fine joints in stonework, with later pointing (before repair in 1986)

Fig 138 Bromham bridge: squared coursed limestone walling, 1902

skilled masons, though at Arlesey the stonework is of a poorer standard and much more variable. The bridges over the Flit at Chicksands and Clophill are composed of thin rubble blocks of stone, suggesting a paucity of supply. On the other hand, the quality of other post-medieval bridges in sandstone at Biggleswade, Girtford and later at Tempsford, approaches or even surpasses that of the masonry at Sutton. Sandstone was generally cut into manageable sizes though monolithic blocks can be found on the upstream voussoirs at Barford phase 2 (late 17th/early 18th century), or in the fascias at Tempsford (1820).

Medieval limestone bridges were nearly all rubble built since the thinly bedded local stone was of limited use as a freestone. However, the stonework was usually regularly coursed though more random rubble occurs in places at Harrold. Well-squared stone in regular courses was used for the 1902 widening at Bromham (Fig 138), and a formalised random walling was adopted at Tymsill bridge and the new Stafford bridge in the 1930's.

Ashlar is first used at St Neots in the early 17th century but really comes into its own with the development of architecturally designed bridges from the late 18th century. Notable examples include ornamental Park features, such as the Basin bridge in Woburn Park (originally faced in clunch), and the lakeside facade of Smeaton's bridge in Southill Park. Of road bridges only Bedford (Fig 135) and Tempsford (the latter mainly in sandstone), are exclusively of ashlar construction, but the 1828 turnpike arches at Turvey (Fig 77) are ashlar faced.

Ashlar was occasionally reused from elsewhere in bridge repairs. Dressed Ketton stone was incorporated into the parapet extension at Sutton, and reused ashlar can be found as patching in Barford bridge, and in post-1857 repairs to Harrold. Finally an attempt to imitate ashlar coursing can be seen at Bromham bridge, where repairs to the 19th century flood arches were carried out with lime-stone and occasionally clunch tiles, squared and set on edge. (Similar masonry occurs at St Cuthbert's church in Bedford, which was rebuilt during 1844-7 only just before the probable date of the Bromham repairs.) However these are late exceptions to a tradition of rubble-built bridges constructed entirely from local material.

Stone was almost always carefully prepared, usually squared off and faced before use. This is especially true for the dressed sandstone but also often for rubble lime-stone. Traces of irregular vertical tool marks may be seen on both stone types. By the early 19th century on the Ivel Navigation bridges these vertical marks become much more regular suggesting the use of a broader chisel. A few other types of tooling occur, though all on isolated stones: criss-crossed diagonal markings have been noted at Tymsill bridge and Brickgate bridge (Blunham), and diamond-shaped peck marks on a limestone block (probably reused) on Blunham river bridge.

None of the rubble limestone spandrel walls repaired in recent years have proved to be very substantial; they usually consisted of no more than the facing stones with one further thickness of stone behind, and the total thickness would typically be about 18 in (500mm). The only exceptions were the solid cutwaters at Bromham which were rebuilt in 1813. Sandstone bridges were found to be of a more substantial nature, particularly at Sutton, where facing stones were mostly of considerable depth with a second course of dressed stone behind.

CORES

As the spandrel walls were built up, the core of the bridge was infilled with a variety of earthy or stony material. At Bromham the core of the medieval bridge was briefly exposed during the excavation for a new drainage outlet at the north end of pier 25/26, and consisted of a series of thinly bedded dumped earths and clays. The infilling of Harrold flood arch 1 comprised clay with stone frag-ments. The demolition of Bedford's medieval bridge revealed 'a great body of Rubbish filled in over the Arches, so that time has made it a sort of solid Mass'.[40]

Rebuilding of the south river abutment at Harrold revealed a sequence which had been complicated by various widenings. The earliest part of the bridge consisted of a rubble wall retaining an earth core. A layer of sandy loam and gravel then formed the make-up for a cobbled surface which may have been in use until the 1857 widening. The core of the 1813 work at Bromham was also exposed during drainage improvements. In contrast to the more varied fill of the medieval bridge, it consisted of dumped clay forming an impervious water-proofing layer.

Contract documents for Tempsford give detailed infor-mation about the nature of the bridge's infill. The extrados of each arch was to be covered with 6 inches (150mm) of clay to act as a waterproofing. Site debris was then to be laid on top to build up the road surface.[41] Trial trenches through the deck in 1993 confirmed that these instructions had been fully implemented: the clay layer over the arches was intact, and the rest of the fill comprised a mixture of loam with sandstone fragments and stone dust.

PARAPETS

Contrary to traditional ideas of medieval bridges with massive stone parapets, it appears that most early bridges had little or nothing in the way of barriers to protect those who used them. Certainly, Harrold foot causeway was completely unfenced until about the 1930s,[42] and a note in the Quarter Sessions bridge minutes for 1819 comments that at Stafford the road was '8 ft 6 in [2.6m] wide in one place and without sidewalls'.[43]

The present parapet at Sutton is an addition to the original bridge, and there may only have been a low kerb when it was first built. The death of William Ferrers in 1254 at St Neots has been interpreted as evidence for the absence of any fencing or walling along the bridge there.[44] The first attempts at greater safety seem to have involved the provision of timber rails. These consisted of joists bedded into the face of the bridge, to which were attached uprights held in place by braces across the angle; horizontal rails were fixed between the uprights. Harrold bridge had a post and rail fence along most of the river bridge in the early 19th century;[45] the stubs of some timber joists can still be seen in the downstream elevation of the bridge immediately below the string course (Fig 70).

Timber fencing was still used on many of the minor bridges in Bedfordshire in the 19th century; Oakley South bridge, where the fence was last renewed in 1987, is an interesting survival of this tradition (Fig 49).

The earliest documentary reference to a parapet is on Bedford bridge in 1526.[46] The presence of a moulded string course over Barford's river arches suggests that there may have been a stone parapet above when it was built in the late 15th century. Fragments of a low stone parapet (possibly original) survive at the 17th century bridge at Blunham, built into a later brick parapet.

Other major bridges were equipped with stone parapets by, or during, the 19th century. At Turvey, drawings of 1824[47] show a stone parapet over the Bedfordshire arches, but wooden railings leading on to the foot causeway. At Stafford, Thomas Fisher's drawing of 1812 shows stone parapets over the river arches[48] (contrary to the Quarter Sessions records of 1819, quoted above). Plans drawn up for alterations to Bromham bridge in 1813[49] confirm that there was a stone parapet over the river arches; the flood arches built by Salmon also included stone parapets. The fencing at Harrold was replaced by a stone parapet when the bridge was widened in 1857.

Parapets or, in the case of Bedford bridge, balustrades were incorporated into all major new bridges from the 18th century onwards. In the 19th century the new iron bridges carried iron rails of varied design, and brick parapets also became common (for example at Barford and Blunham).

ROAD SURFACES

Most evidence for surfacing materials is derived from documentary sources. Quarter Sessions records provide

Fig 139 Barford bridge: 18th century cobble and limestone road surfacing

frequent references to gravel for surfacing and for infilling ruts.

Several exposures of historic road surfaces have been recorded during trial trenching or resurfacing work. The best preserved is at Barford bridge, consisting of a mixture of cobbles, and both pitched and paved limestone (Fig 139). The limestone appeared to be in strips running along the bridge, perhaps designed for the wheels of vehicles. The surface covered the whole bridge except the 19th century additions and widening, and must therefore date after the flood arches were built in the late 17th/early 18th century (possibly laid as part of that phase of alteration). It has been preserved intact beneath the latest modern road surfacing.

Traces of compacted gravel surfaces were exposed during drainage operations at Bromham, along with pitched limestone and cobbled surfaces. Fragments of pitched limestone survived on the river bridge at Harrold, whilst by the early 20th century the foot causeway had a cobbled surface constructed from river borne pebbles.[50]

Wing's specifications for Bedford bridge[51] included Scotch stone for paving but at Tempsford Savage preferred screened gravel to be laid directly onto the bridge's fill.[52] During resurfacing in 1994, this was located in places under the raised modern carriageway, and consists of angular granite fragments compacted into a very hard surface, typical of 18th and 19th century metalling techniques.

INVERTS

Several bridges in the county have well preserved inverts protecting the floors of arches from scour. The most notable and visible examples can be found in limestone, at Bromham (where several were reset in 1986) and Felmersham, and in brick at the Tempsford flood arches. Less well preserved stone inverts have been observed or recorded at Turvey, Harrold, Radwell, Kempston, Barford, Blunham river bridge and Arlesey, and in brick at many late 19th and early 20th century bridges. Many of these surfaces are in a very poor condition or have been replaced or covered in concrete.

There is no evidence that formal stone inverts were a feature of the medieval bridge, and the earliest inverts in Bedfordshire are undated. An intact invert which was recorded under the east arch at Blunham in 1992 fitted very closely to the pier bases and may have been part of the original 17th century construction. It was in limestone, part paved and part pitched, and extended upstream to protect the adjacent cutwater. Its outer limit was defined by a horizontal timber beam. A similar invert has been identified at Bromham, associated with the cart bridge which stood south of the main causeway in the 18th century.

A site at Kempston, previously interpreted as a Roman ford,[53] was almost certainly the invert of Cater's Great Bridge, which was in use by 1666 until the mid-19th century.[54]

The practice of laying inverts as an integral part of bridge construction was widespread by the 18th century. Usually they were 'framed and sett', whereby timber frames were laid flat on the river bed, often with short fixing piles driven vertically down. The frames were then packed with large squared stones or 'setts' not easily disturbed by the current, thus protecting the river bed from scouring especially during floods.[55] The earliest dated example is Essex bridge, Dublin (1753) where a 'thorough' foundation was laid across the river bed, piers and openings alike. Sheet piling, 6 inches (150mm) thick, was set at the edges beyond the cutwaters.[56]

Framed and sett inverts were not without their drawbacks. Smeaton preferred a concave stone bed, with its interstices filled with gravel and sand, as the wooden elements of framed and sett inverts could decay and work loose leading to the break up of the protective surface.[57] For bridges over smaller rivers he favoured a complete platform of stone or timber held in place by sheet piles laid over the entire river bed. For his bridge at Cardington, he used a brick invert stretched round the whole bridge extending to the tips of the cutwaters and held in place by a wooden frame within a series of upright piles. The original brickwork has now either been replaced or covered in concrete. The southernmost arch at Felmersham bridge, which is normally dry and can therefore be easily inspected, is also framed in timber. The pitched stones which run parallel to the carriageway are contained within sill beams, themselves held in place by short upright piles, immediately outside the line of the arches. A further stretch of invert upstream consists of large paving slabs in contrast to the fine coursing in the framed and sett part and may be additional.

Drawings of Barford bridge in 1939[58] show stone inverts beneath a number of the river arches, some with horizontal timbers immediately downstream. Trial pits in 1983 also located horizontal timbers downstream of some of the flood arches.[59] Since the outer sill beam was traced over the full length of the bridge the construction of the apron and therefore the invert must date from after the construction of the flood arches.

In contrast, the inverts at Bromham, laid in 1813-14, were not constructed within a timber framework. They were composed of roughly squared limestone blocks set either parallel with, or at right angles to, the carriageway, and some had a spine of larger limestone blocks running down the centre. Areas of flat paving probably indicate later repairs. The pitched stonework originally extended either side of the bridge and round the cutwaters, to protect from scour; a large area survives south of arch 20, nearest the river.

The flood arches at Tempsford, also early 19th century, were lined with brick inverts, but there is no evidence of inverts under the river arches. In the south of the county, a different method was proposed in the contract specifications for Horsepool bridge, Luton, 1838: 'the ground or flooring under the arches to consist of well pounded chalk and gravel laid in courses 6 in [150mm] thick and to be well rammed and consolidated'. During the 19th century brick was increasingly used to construct inverts for the many minor bridges in the county, before the universal adoption of concrete by the 20th century.

Inverts are occasionally found beneath medieval arches, as at Harrold, Turvey and Arlesey. However, entries in the Quarter Sessions for Arlesey bridge, 1808,[60] and for paving the floor of arch 11 at Harrold in 1824,[61] serve as reminders that these works could be inserted at a much later date.

NOTES

1 T P Smith, 'The Anglo-Saxon Churches of Bedfordshire', *Bedfordshire Archaeol J* 3, 1966, 7-14
2 S E Rigold, 1975, 'Structural aspects of medieval bridges', *Medieval Archaeology* 19, 48-91, esp 49-51
3 M L J Rowlands, *Monnow Bridge and Gate,* 1994
4 L Cooper, S Ripper and P Clay, 'The Hemington Bridges', *Current Archaeology* 140, Sep/Nov 1994, 316-321
5 RCHME, *Huntingdonshire,* 1926, 151-152, 215-216
6 C Gorham, *History of St Neots,* 1820, 336-338
7 W Austin, *The History of Luton and its Hamlets,* vol I, 1928, 246
8 Beds RO: X 261/156-7
9 Beds RO: BC 536
10 Beds RO: L 26/573
11 Beds RO: KK 769
12 Gorham, *op cit*
13 Beds RO: QSX 18, 1824
14 Beds RO: QBC 2, 1855
15 G Notcutt & C Eccles, 'The Geology of Bedfordshire Churches', *Beds Mag* 20 no 160, Spring 1987, 341-347
16 Beds RO: KK 944
17 Beds RO: KK 944/4; HER 11133
18 Beds RO: KK 944/4; HER 11134
19 Beds RO: CH 219-228; HER 11130

20 S R Coleman, *Leighton Buzzard Parish Survey,* Beds County Council, unpub, 1981 (copy in Heritage Group, County Hall)

21 eg Beds RO: L 4/53, 1655 – 'hills and waste ground called Round Hill and Slade Ground and the stone pits thereon'

22 Beds RO: KK 769

23 RCHME, *Huntingdonshire,* 1926, 224

24 Alan Cox, *Survey of Bedfordshire: Brickmaking,* 1979, 34

25 E A Labrum (ed), *Civil Engineering Heritage: Eastern & Central England,* Institute of Civil Engineers, 1994, 183

26 See *Beds Mag* 22 no 169, Summer 1989, 43 for a copy of a Moreton and Kinman advertisement

27 Ruddock, 1979, 201-202, who quotes: Palladio A, *I quattro libri dell' architecttura,* 1570 and Gautier H, *Dissertation sur les culees, 'voussoirs, piles et poussees des ponts* (Paris 1717). These and other examples are also discussed in Mesqui, 1986

28 *Current Archaeology* 122, Nov 1990, 73-76

29 Beds RO: W 1/81

30 Beds RO: X 67/934/60

31 Renn, 1974

32 *ibid,* 75

33 *ibid,* 80-81

34 Beds RO: QBM 1, 25

35 Beds RO: FN 1253, 81-85

36 Jervoise, 1932, 94

37 English Heritage Ancient monument record form for Blunham bridge

38 S W Brown, 'The Medieval Bridge and St Gabriel's Chapel at Bishop's Clyst', *Proc Devon Archaeol Soc* 40, 1982, 163-169, esp p168

39 Jervoise, 1932, 97 n5

40 Beds RO: W 1/81

41 Beds RO: QBP 8/4

42 Beds RO: Slide 3559

43 Beds RO: QBM 1, 114

44 R Young, 'St Neots bridge', *St Neots Local History Magazine,* Summer 1983, 16-17

45 Beds RO: PB 6/1

46 Broade, 1526, 'Peregrination', quoted by W N Henman, 'Bedford bridge and its story', *Beds Times,* 31.10.1913

47 Beds RO: QSX 18

48 Beds RO: X 376/40

49 Beds RO: PB 7/2

50 Beds RO: Slide 3559

51 Beds RO: Micf 15, Bedford Improvements Commission, 3.11.1809

52 Beds RO: QBP 8/4

53 Viatores, *Roman Roads in the South-East Midlands,* 1964, 281-282

54 J Wood, *Kempston parish survey,* 1984, 24-26

55 Ruddock, 1979, 26

56 *ibid,* 43

57 *ibid,* 93

58 Drawings by Great Ouse Catchment Board, copies in HER

59 Co Engineer drawing BR/C5/180/8

60 Beds RO: QSR 1808, 109

61 Beds RO: QSR 27, 1825, 499

APPENDIX 1 – Chronological table

This table includes those bridges where significant structural evidence survives or has been recorded. Dates in brackets give the first documentary reference to a bridge of which the construction date is unknown.

Date	Nene valley	Ouse valley	Ivel valley	Lea valley	Navigation
Medieval		Turvey (1136/38)			
Medieval		Harrold (1136/46)			
Medieval		Bedford (12th c)			
Medieval		Bromham (1224)			
Medieval		St Neots (1254)			
Medieval			Arlesey (1466/67?)		
Medieval			Sutton (1504)		
Medieval		Stafford (1505)			
Medieval		Tymsill (1507)			
Medieval			Clay, Clifton (1527)		
?Medieval			Langford (1765)		
15th c		Barford river arches			
1588-1617		St Neots rebuilt			
17th c			Blunham		
c.1704		Barford flood arches			
1766		Radwell			
1778		Cardington			
1779	Hinwick				
1780			Girtford		
1796			Biggleswade		
18th c			Chicksands		
18th c			Clophill		
1800					Grand Junction Canal
1813		Wing's bridge, Bedford			
1814		Bromham flood arches			
1815		Oakley			
1818		Felmersham			
1819			Langford iron bridge		
1820		Tempsford stone bridge			
1823			Broom iron bridge		
1823					Ivel Navigation
1824			Clay, Clifton iron bridge		
1828		Turvey turnpike arches			
1828			Shefford iron bridges		
1831				Hyde	
1838				Horsepool/North	
1849		Stafford new causeway			
1895			Tannery, Potton		
1895			Flitwick		
1898			Eaton Bray		

APPENDIX 2 – Summary county map

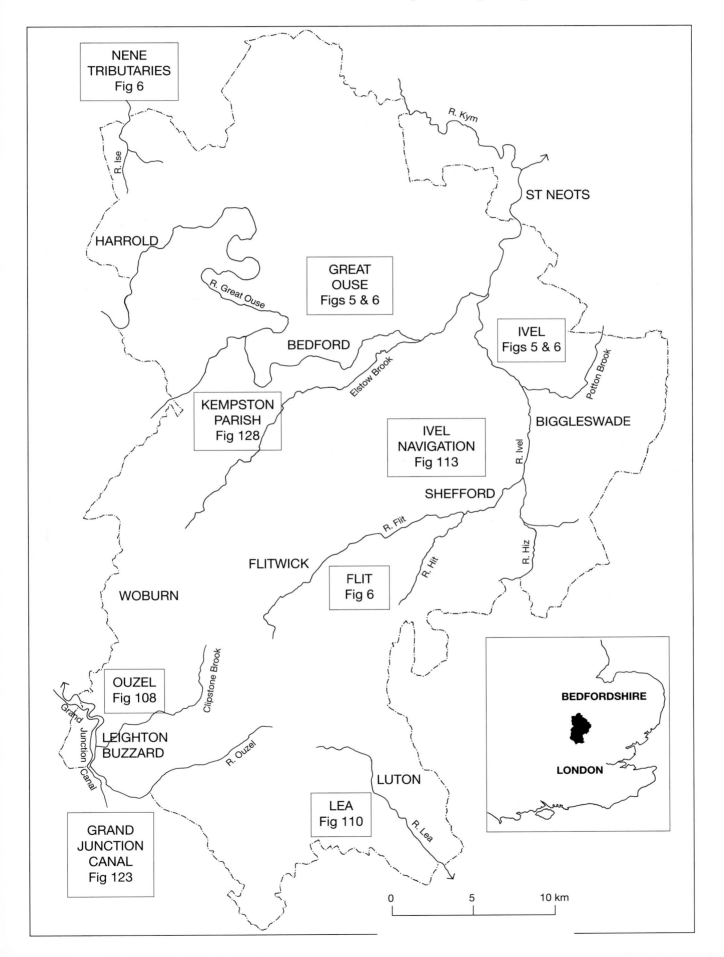

NENE
TRIBUTARIES
Fig 6

R. Kym

ST NEOTS

R. Ise

HARROLD

R. Great Ouse

GREAT
OUSE
Figs 5 & 6

BEDFORD

IVEL
Figs 5 & 6

Potton Brook

Elstow Brook

KEMPSTON
PARISH
Fig 128

IVEL
NAVIGATION
Fig 113

BIGGLESWADE

R. Ivel

SHEFFORD

R. Flit

R. Hit

R. Hiz

FLITWICK

FLIT
Fig 6

WOBURN

Clipstone Brook

OUZEL
Fig 108

Grand Junction Canal

LEIGHTON
BUZZARD

R. Ouzel

LUTON

GRAND
JUNCTION
CANAL
Fig 123

LEA
Fig 110

R. Lea

BEDFORDSHIRE

LONDON

0   5   10 km

GLOSSARY

TECHNICAL TERMS

Abutment: the walls at the river bank which support the ends of an arch

Arch: a curved structure supporting and carrying a weight across a gap. Formed by the arrangement of stones or bricks which combine to push down and transfer the thrust to the sides. In bridges the arches are supported by piers or abutments which take the load

Arch ring: the exposed face or edge of an arch, visible on the elevation of a bridge. It is usually composed of a single or double order of voussoir stones

Arris: the edge at the intersection of two surfaces of a stone or brick

Ashlar: a high quality masonry form, the stones being carefully cut to fit regular courses and separated by very thin joints

Balustrade: an ornamental railing of balusters executed in stone supporting a coping. In bridges this feature forms the parapet

Baluster: a small moulded pillar, usually circular in section, swelling towards the base

Beam: a straight or slightly curved structural component of iron bridges which supports loads and transfers them to the piers or abutments

Cantilever: bracket used to support a beam fixed at one end but unsupported elsewhere. Sometimes used as a means of widening a bridge to carry a footpath

Cast iron: a form of iron, shaped whilst molten by pouring into moulds; less subject to corrosion than wrought iron

Centering (formwork): a temporary work in timber, to support and shape an arch during construction. Once the arch had set the centering was struck (removed)

Chamfer: the trimming off or paring of the edge or arris between two surfaces, usually at a 45° angle. Broad chamfers seem to be earlier in Bedfordshire masonry than narrow chamfers.

Coffer dam: a temporary structure constructed in the river to form an area from which water can be excluded or pumped out enabling pier foundations to be constructed on a dry river bed.

Coping: the capping of a parapet. Usually of angled or curved stone or brick, often with an overhang to throw water off the parapet face below.

Corbel: a projecting stone to support a roof timber

Corbelling: a means of carrying stonework over a void, each course slightly overhanging the one below

Core: the packing or make-up between the upper surface of an arch and the road surface

Cornes de vache: an elaborate form of chamfering. The chamfer tapers from the arch springing towards the crown.

Cross rib: a form of arch construction in which a strengthening rib of stone runs across an arch from one arch ring to the other

Crown: the highest, or centre part of the arch. The arch ring in later bridges is often decorated by a raised keystone at this point

Cutwater: an extension of the face of a pier to deflect flowing water. In medieval Bedfordshire bridges the cutwaters are pointed, or keeled, on the upstream face only but in other areas both upstream and downstream faces can be keeled. Post-medieval bridges display a greater variety of forms

Deck: the surface or roadway of a bridge

Double order: an arch in which two rows of voussoirs form one arch ring inside another

Dressed: a form of masonry where the stone has been squared off. Generally the stonework is not of as high quality as ashlar and the joints are thicker and more variable

Elliptical: a form of arch, in which the curves are formed by radii from three centres

Extrados: the outer, exposed surface, of an arch (same as soffit)

Fill: see core

Flange: a flat projection set at right angles on iron girders

Framed and set(t): the stones of a surface set on edge and framed in a timber surround

Freestone: stone which may be cut into regular blocks and worked with a chisel

Girder: originally a large beam of wood but later also an iron beam

Gothic: in bridges, specifically the pointed arch, but more generally a major medieval architectural style

Grouting: the injection under pressure of liquid binding material into voids in masonry

Haunch: the part of the arch midway between the springing and the crown

Intrados: the interior or upper surface of an arch; generally only visible in the course of excavation of the deck above

Invert: the paved floor of an arch

Keeled: the pointed shape of a cutwater, like the keel of a boat

Keystone: stone at the crown of the arch, usually raised or projecting. So called because it was the last stone to be placed in the arch. Often slighter broader than the gap, it would be forced into the space, channeling extra pressure on to the piers/abutments.

Lattice: criss-cross pattern seen on some of the railings of the Moreton and Kinman iron bridges

Offset: a projection from the main vertical face of a pier or abutment

Parapet: a stone or brick wall of a bridge above the road surface

Photogrammetry: a method of producing an accurate drawing of stonework through stereoscopic photographs

Pier: The solid support of a bridge on which the arches rest

Pile: vertically driven timber support for pier or abutment

Pointing: the mortar or cement finish applied to face masonry or brick joints

Puddled clay: clay mixed with water, and sometimes sand, to reach a uniformly plastic and impermeable state

Quatrefoil: a decorative motif, representing four leaves symmetrically arranged

Quoin: corner

Raft: timber foundation platform

Rectified photography: a method of producing an accurate drawing of stonework through photographs which are printed to exact scale

Refuge: a recess in the parapet wall , usually triangular, formed by the extension of keeled cutwaters up to the carriageway. Called a refuge because pedestrians could step back from the line of the traffic Ribs: projecting bands of voussoir stones which, on bridges, took the weight of the arch, reducing the amount of stone to be accurately hewn to about a third.

(Road) Plates: on iron bridges, the iron plates which rested between the girders, on which the gravel of the road surface was laid

Rubble: a form of masonry, applied to quarried stone of random size and shape

Scantling: small timbers, usually used in temporary structures (eg scaffolding or formwork) during bridge construction or repair

Scour: the erosive action of currents in the water against the river bed and the bridge piers and abutments

Skew: a method of arch construction, when a bridge crosses a river obliquely but the soffit coursing is perpendicular to the long axis of the arch

Sleeper beam: a timber beam laid flat to form a level base for a structure above

Soffit: the exposed underside of an arch, same as extrados

Span: the distance between the piers or abutments of an arch

Spandrel: the triangular area above the arch, defined by lines extending vertically from the springing and horizontally from the crown; or the area between the level of the roadway (often marked by the string course) and the arch or two adjacent arches

Springing: the point from which an arch begins to turn from the pier or abutment

Staunch: an early form of lock, in which water was held back to allow boats to pass

String course: a projecting horizontal course, often moulded, forming a dripstone to throw water away from the face of the bridge

Stucco: plaster surface coating a wall

Tie: a metal rod inserted through the structure of the bridge to pull it together

Trestle: a form of timber construction in which vertical members support a horizontal structure, strengthened by braces

Underpinning: the strengthening of arch foundations by excavation below the basal course to insert additional courses or piles

Voussoirs: wedge-shaped stones which combine to give an arch ring strength

Wing wall: the extension of the parapet wall onto the approaches of a bridge, usually seen to splay outwards

Wrought iron: or malleable iron, a form of iron which is easily forged under heat but subject to corrosion

HISTORICAL TERMS

Assizes: a judicial sitting or session

Burh: a fortified Saxon town

Causey: causeway

Chantry chapel: a chapel in which a priest was paid to say masses and pray for the souls of the dead

Coroner's Rolls: records of the Coroner's court, which sat in cases of unnatural death

Dissolution: the closure of monasteries in the 16th century

Hue: pursuit of a criminal

Hundred: an administrative subdivision of a county, comprising a group of parishes

Hundred Rolls: records of inquiries commissioned by Edward I into various land-holding rights

Indulgences: remission of punishment for sins in return for pious donations

Justices of the Peace: an magistrate appointed to represent the crown in keeping law and order, and administering the affairs of a county

Messuage: a dwelling house or homestead and the site occupied by it

Pontage: a grant by the crown of the right to charge tolls to cross a bridge

Present/presentment: to charge an individual before a court (eg manor court or Quarter Sessions) for failure to discharge duties

Quarter Sessions: quarterly meeting of the Justices of the Peace

Sauvetage: place of safety

Sheriff: royal official responsible for the administration of a county (= 'shire reeve')

Terminus ante quem: a date before which something must have happened

Tithes: a tenth part of the produce of the land, paid to the church. Commuted to an annual rent in 1836

HISTORIC MEASUREMENTS

Throughout the text, measurements are given in both imperial and metric. Contrary to normal practice, imperial measurements are given first, because these are often derived directly from historic documentation.

Linear

1 inch	= 25.4 millimetres
1 foot = 12 inches	= 0.3048 metre

Volume

1 bushel = 8 gallons = 64 pints	= 36.4 litres
1 quarter = 8 bushels	= 2.91 hectolitres

Weight

1 pound (lb)	= 0.4536 kilogram
1 stone = 14 pounds	= 6.35 kilograms
1 hundredweight (cwt) = 8 stones	= 50.8 kilograms
1 ton = 20 cwt	= 1.016 tonnes

Money

1 shilling (1s) = 12 pence (12d)	= 5p	
£1 = 20s = 240d		
1 mark (two-thirds of a pound)	= 13s 4d	= approx 67p
1 angel (one-third of a pound)	= 6s 8d	= approx 33p
1 noble (one-sixth of a pound)	= 3s 4d	= approx 17p

It is difficult to give a precise value for the £ in previous centuries, and therefore to compare the cost of bridge-building and repair with modern prices. However, an agricultural labourer's wages can give some idea of the scale of change: for a day's work the pay was 4d in 1568, 8d in 1688, 1s in 1760 and 1s 4d in 1788. A Victorian labourer earned 10s per week. More detailed discussion can be found in L Munby, *How Much is That Worth?*, Br Assoc of Local History, 1996 and C R Chapman, *How Heavy, How Much and How Long?*, Lochin Publishing, 1995.

SUMMARY

Repairs carried out to Bedfordshire's historic bridges between 1982 and 1994 were accompanied by detailed historical research and archaeological recording. This enabled the analysis of the county's bridges as a group of monuments, investigating the effects of local topography, maintenance liabilities, transport needs, the availability of raw materials, and the influence of wider architectural developments on local bridge construction. A group of major medieval bridges and associated foot causeways in the Ouse valley is noted as of particular importance. A number of 18th and 19th century bridges display the adoption of new architectural and engineering techniques, while other bridges of the same period continue in traditional local style. Bridges of the early 19th century Grand Junction Canal and Ivel Navigation are also discussed, and a summaries of historical references to bridges in each river valley demonstrate the complexity of local communications.

Résumé

Entre 1982 and 1994 les divers services de Bedfordshire County Council ont effectué une opération de réparations, de travaux archéologiques et de recherches historiques approfondies sur les ponts anciens de département. Cela nous a permis d'analyser les ponts de Bedfordshire en tant que groupe de monuments, en examinant les effets de la topographie régionale, les obligations d'entretien, les besoins du transport, la disponabilité des matières premières et l'influence des développements architecturaux généralisés sur la construction des ponts dans la région. Nous avons porté notre attention plus particulièrement sur un groupe d'importants ponts médiévaux et leurs chaussées attenantes dans la vallée de la rivière Ouse. L'adoption de nouvelles techniques d'architecture et de génie civil est mise en évidence dans la construction de plusieurs ponts datant du XVIIIe et du XIXe siècles, tandis que d'autres ponts de la même époque gardent le style traditionnel caractéristique de cette région. Nous présentons également les ponts du XIXe siècle qui traversent le Grand Junction Canal et la Ivel Navigation. Finalement, en considérant les autres ponts de chaque vallée, pour la plupart connus seulement par des documents historiques, les auteurs démontrent la complexité des communications dans la région.

Zusammenfassung

Reparaturen an den historischen Brücken Bedfordshires, die in den Jahren von 1982 bis 1994 ausgeführt wurden, ermöglichten es, historische und archaelogische Nachforschungen auszuführen und dokumentarisch festzuhalten.

Es war dadurch möglich, in der Auswertung der hiesigen Brücken diese als eine Denkmalgruppe zu behandeln, indem die Effekte untersucht wurden, die sich aus der Topographie, Reparaturen und Unterhalt, Transportbedürfnissen, örtlich vorhandenem Baumaterial und dem Einfluss auf den lokalen Brückenbau aus Entwicklungen im Gebiet der Architektur, ergeben.

Besonders wichtig ist eine Gruppe von mittelalterlichen Brücken und den dazugehörenden Fussgängerdämmen im Ouse Tal.

An einigen Brücken aus dem 18. und 19. Jahrhundert kann man deutlich die neuen, von Architeken und Ingineuren entwickelten Techniken erkennen, während andere, zur gleichen Zeit gebaute Brücken, weiterhin im Ortsstil gebaut wurden. Brücken über den Grand Junction Kanal und die Ivel Navigation aus dem frühen 19. Jahrhundert werden ebenfalls besprochen; und die Zusammenfassung des historischen Quellenmaterials für die Brücken jedes Flusstals zeigt deutlich wie kompliziert die örtlichen Verkehrsverbindungen gewesen sind.

BIBLIOGRAPHY

Individual references are cited in the relevant footnotes. The following publications are of general interest.

Bidwell, P T, & Holbrook, N, 1989, *Hadrian's Wall Bridges,* English Heritage Archaeological Report no 9

Blackwall, A, 1985, *Historic Bridges of Shropshire* (Shrewsbury)

Boyer, M, 1976, *Medieval French Bridges: A History* (Cambridge, Mass)

Collingwood, W G, 1928, 'Packhorse Bridges', *Transactions of the Cumberland and Westmorland Antiquarian Society* 28, 120-128

de Maré, E, 1975, *Bridges of Britain* (Batsford, London)

de Maré, E, 1987, *The Canals of England* (Alan Sutton)

Deyber, A, 1977, 'Le pont celtique d'Etival-Clairefontaine (Vosges)', *Revue Archeologique de l'Est et du Centre-est* 29, 105-116 (Dijon)

Deyber, A, 1980, 'Du nouveau a propos du pont celtique D'Etival-Clairefontaine (Vosges)', *Revue Archeologique de l'Est et du Centre-est* 31, 57-59 (Dijon)

Godber, J, 1969, *History of Bedfordshire* (Bedfordshire County Council)

Goodfellow, P, 1985/86, 'Medieval Bridges in Northamptonshire', *Northamptonshire Past and Present* 7 no 3, 143-158

Harrison, D, 1990, 'Medieval Bridges', *Current Archaeology* no 122, 73-76

Henderson, C & Coates, H, 1928, reprinted 1972, *Old Cornish Bridges & Streams* (Truro)

Henderson, C & Jervoise, E, 1938, *Old Devon Bridges* (Wheaton)

Hinchliffe, E, 1994, *A Guide to the Packhorse Bridges of Britain* (Milnthorpe)

Home, G, 1931, *Old London Bridge* (London)

Inglis, H R G, 1911-12, 'The ancient bridges in Scotland, and their relation to Roman and medieval bridges in Europe', *Proceedings of the Society of Antiquaries of Scotland* 46, 151-177

Jervoise, E, 1932, reprinted 1973, *The Ancient Bridges of Mid and Eastern England* (Architectural Press, London)

Jervoise, E, 1936, reprinted 1976, *The Ancient Bridges of Wales and Western England* (Architectural Press, London)

Labrum, E A (ed), 1994, *Civil Engineering Heritage: Eastern & Central England* (Institute of Civil Engineers)

Mawer, A & Stenton, F M, 1926, *The Placenames of Bedfordshire and Huntingdonshire,* English Placenames Society vol 3

McKeague, P, 1987, 'Bedfordshire Bridges', *Bedfordshire Magazine* 21 no 162, 63-64

McKeague, P and Cook, M, 1991, 'South Bedfordshire Bridges', *Bedfordshire Magazine* 22 no 176, 333-335

Mesqui, J, 1986, *Le Pont avant l'heure des Ingenieurs* (Paris)

Mesqui, J, 1994, *Chemins et Ponts: Lien entre les Hommes* (Paris)

O'Keeffe, P & Simington, T, 1991, *Irish Stone Bridges: History and Heritage* (Irish Academic Press/Irish DOE)

Pevsner, N, 1968, *The Buildings of England: Bedfordshire and the County of Huntingdon and Peterborough* (Penguin)

Prade, M, 1986, *Les Ponts Monuments Historiques* (Poitiers)

Prade, M, 1988, *Ponts et Viaducts au xixe siecle: Techniques Nouvelles et Grands Realisations Francaises* (Poitiers)

Renn, D F, 1974, 'The River Wey Bridges between Farnham and Guildford', *Research volume of the Surrey Archaeological Society* 1, 75-83 (Guildford)

Rigold, S E, 1975, 'Structural aspects of medieval bridges', *Medieval Archaeology* 19, 48-91

Ruddock, T, 1979, *Arch bridges and their builders 1735-1835* (Cambridge)

Steane, J, 1981, *Medieval Bridges in Oxfordshire,* Oxfordshire Museums Information Sheet 17 (Oxfordshire County Council)

Webb, S & Webb, B, 1913, *English Local Government: the Story of the King's Highway* (London)

INDEX

PEOPLE

SUBJECTS

Printed by Stanley L. Hunt (Printers) Ltd, Midland Road, Rushden, Northants